总 策 划　　许　琳
总 监 制　　马箭飞　　　戚德祥
监　 制　　彭增安　　张彤辉　　　王锦红　　　王　飙

主　 编　　刘　珣
编　 者　　张　凯　　刘社会　　　陈　曦　　　左珊丹
　　　　　　施家炜　　刘　珣

出 版 人　　戚德祥
项目组长　　王　飙
中文编辑　　王亚莉
英语编辑　　侯晓娟
英语审订　　余心乐
美术设计　　张　静　　申真真

国家汉办/孔子学院总部
Hanban (Confucius Institute Headquarters)

新实用汉语课本

New Practical Chinese Reader

主 编 刘 珣

编 者 张 凯   刘社会   陈 曦
        左珊丹   施家炜   刘 珣

For Beginners

汉字册
Learning Chinese Characters

北京语言大学出版社
BEIJING LANGUAGE AND CULTURE
UNIVERSITY PRESS

图书在版编目（CIP）数据

新实用汉语课本汉字册：英语版 /刘珣主编.
—北京：北京语言大学出版社，2011.7
　ISBN 978-7-5619-3061-8

　Ⅰ.①新…　Ⅱ.①刘…　Ⅲ.①汉语—对外汉语教学—习题集
Ⅳ.①H195.4

　中国版本图书馆CIP数据核字（2011）第129440号

书　　　名：	新实用汉语课本汉字册：英语版	
责任印制：	汪学发	

出版发行：北京语言大学出版社

社　　址：	北京市海淀区学院路 15 号	邮政编码：	100083
网　　址：	www.blcup.com		
电　　话：	国内发行 8610-82303650/3591/3651		
	海外发行 8610-82300309/0361/3080/3365		
	编辑部 8610-82303647/3592		
	读者服务部 8610-82303653/3908		
	网上订购电话 8610-82303668		
	客户服务信箱 service@blcup.net		
印　　刷：	北京画中画印刷有限公司		
经　　销：	全国新华书店		

版　　次：	2011年7月第1版　2011年7月第1次印刷
开　　本：	880毫米×1194毫米　1/16　印张：7.75
字　　数：	105千字
书　　号：	ISBN 978-7-5619-3061-8 /H.11102
	02500

凡有印装质量问题，本社负责调换。电话：8610-82303590

Printed in China.

To the students

Welcome to *Learning Chinese Characters* of *New Practical Chinese Reader*!

New Practical Chinese Reader consists of three books, *Textbook, Instructor's Manual* and *Learning Chinese Characters*, to meet the needs of both teachers and students of Chinese as a second language.

Learning Chinese Characters is mainly designed for YOU, the students, to use for after-class practice. Each lesson has two parts. In the first part, Learning Chinese Characters, some character components are introduced, and then you are shown how the components are combined to form characters in the text. Rules for constructing and writing characters are also given to facilitate the learning of Chinese characters. In the second part, Writing Exercises, a variety of exercises are provided for you to practice writing characters.

You will find this book most useful to you. Come on then. Let's start to learn Chinese characters. Remember:

Practice makes perfect.

CONTENTS 目录

I

一　汉字学习　Learning Chinese Characters

Chinese characters originated from pictures. The history of their formation is very long, dating back to remote antiquity. Present-day Chinese characters, which evolved from ancient Chinese characters, are square-shaped. Here are some examples illustrating their long evolution:

Picture	Oracle Bone Inscription	Small Seal Character	Official Script	Traditional Chinese in Regular Script	Simplified Chinese in Regular Script
	馬	馬	馬	馬	马

1 汉字基本笔画　Basic strokes of Chinese characters

Chinese characters are written by combining various kinds of "strokes". These strokes can be divided into "basic" strokes and "combined" strokes.

Basic Stroke	Name	Example	Way to Write
丶　↘	diǎn	门	The dot is written from top to bottom-right, as in the first stroke of "门".
一　→	héng	一	The horizontal stroke is written from left to right.

1

Basic Stroke	Name	Example	Way to Write
丨 ↓	shù	木	The vertical stroke is written from top to bottom, as in the second stroke of "木".
丿 ノ	piě	力	The left-falling stroke is written from top to bottom-left, as in the second stroke of "力".
乀 ↘	nà	八	The right-falling stroke is written from top to bottom-right, as in the second stroke of "八".
／ ↗	tí	我	The upward stroke is written from bottom-left to top-right, as in the fourth stroke of "我".

2 认写基本汉字 Learn and write basic Chinese characters

(1) 一　　一
yī　　one　　1 stroke

(2) 八　　丿八
bā　　eight　　2 strokes

(3) 力　　フ力
lì　　strength　　2 strokes

(4) 门（門）　　丶亅门
mén　　door　　3 strokes

(5) 也　　フ力也
yě　　too, also　　3 strokes

(6) 马（馬）　　フ马马
mǎ　　horse　　3 strokes

(7) 女　　　く 女 女
nǚ　　　female　　　　　　　3 strokes

Note: "女" is written as "女" on the left side of a character.

(8) 五　　　一 丆 五 五
wǔ　　　five　　　　　　　4 strokes

(9) 木　　　一 十 才 木
mù　　　wood　　　　　　　4 strokes

Note: "木" is written as "才" on the left side of a character.

(10) 火　　　丶 丷 少 火
huǒ　　　fire　　　　　　　4 strokes

Note: "火" is written as "灬" on the bottom of a character.

3 认写课文中的汉字　Learn and write the Chinese character in the text

林 lín

林 → 才 + 木　　　　　　　8 strokes

二　书写练习　Writing Exercises

1 按正确的笔顺描汉字，并在后边的空格里写汉字。

Trace over the characters, following the correct stroke order. Then copy the characters in the blank spaces.

一	一	一	一						
八	丿 八	八	八						
力	𠃌 力	力	力						

门	` ⺆ 门	门	门						
也	⺄ ⺇ 也	也	也						
马	⺇ 马 马	马	马						
女	⺄ ⺉ 女	女	女						
五	一 丆 五 五	五	五						
木	一 十 才 木	木	木						
火	` ⺀ ⺌ 火	火	火						

2 在空格里写汉字，注意汉字的部件。

Write the characters in the blank spaces, paying attention to the character components.

lín	木 + 木	林							

3 为每个汉字标注拼音，并找到与它相应的图片，然后连线。

Give the *pinyin* of the following characters and find the corresponding drawings. Draw a line to connect the two.

（1）木

（2）女

（3）门

（4）火

（5）马

4 不看课本，尽量写出本课出现的汉字。

Write as many characters as you can from this lesson without reading the textbook.

_____

_____

_____

第二课
Lesson 2

你 忙 吗

一 汉字学习 Learning Chinese Characters

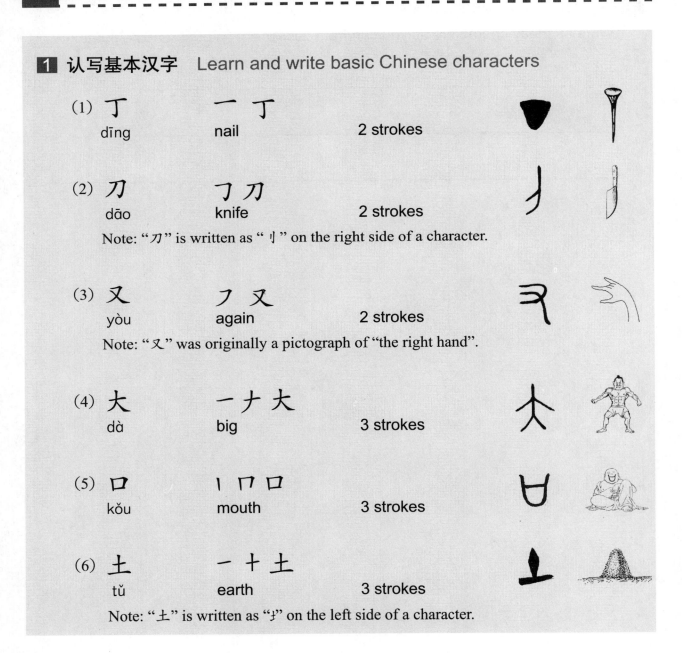

1 认写基本汉字 Learn and write basic Chinese characters

(1) 丁　　一 丁
dīng　　nail　　　　2 strokes

(2) 刀　　フ 刀
dāo　　knife　　　2 strokes
Note: "刀" is written as "刂" on the right side of a character.

(3) 又　　フ 又
yòu　　again　　　2 strokes
Note: "又" was originally a pictograph of "the right hand".

(4) 大　　一 ナ 大
dà　　big　　　　3 strokes

(5) 口　　丨 冂 口
kǒu　　mouth　　　3 strokes

(6) 土　　一 十 土
tǔ　　earth　　　3 strokes
Note: "土" is written as "扌" on the left side of a character.

(7) 六　　　　　丶一六六

liù　　　　　six　　　　　　　　　　　　4 strokes

(8) 不　　　　　一丆才不

bù　　　　　no, not　　　　　　　　　　4 strokes

(9) 尼　　　　　⁻冂尸尸尼

ní　　　　　nun　　　　　　　　　　　　5 strokes

(10) 可　　　　　一丆币叮可

kě　　　　　can, may　　　　　　　　　5 strokes

2 认写课文中的汉字　Learn and write the Chinese characters in the text

(1) 吗 ma （嗎）

吗 → 口 + 马　　　　　　　　　　6 strokes

("口" denotes the meaning of speaking, "马(mǎ)" denotes the pronunciation.)

(2) 呢 ne

呢 → 口 + 尼　　　　　　　　　　8 strokes

("口" denotes the meaning of speaking, "尼(ní)" denotes the pronunciation.)

(3) 妈妈 māma （媽媽）

妈 → 女 + 马　　　　　　　　　　6 strokes

("女" denotes the meaning of woman, "马(mǎ)" denotes the pronunciation.)

(4) 哥哥 gēge

哥 → 可 + 可　　　　　　　　　　10 strokes

二 书写练习 Writing Exercises

1 按正确的笔顺描汉字，并在后边的空格里写汉字。

Trace over the characters, following the correct stroke order. Then copy the characters in the blank spaces.

丁	一丁	丁	丁						
刀	丁刀	刀	刀						
又	丁又	又	又						
大	一ナ大	大	大						
口	丨冂口	口	口						
土	一十土	土	土						
六	丶亠六六	六	六						
不	一丆不不	不	不						
尼	一丆尸尸尼	尼	尼						
可	一丅丆可可	可	可						

2 在空格里写汉字，注意汉字的部件。

Write the characters in the blank spaces, paying attention to the character components.

ma	口＋马	吗					
ne	口＋尼	呢					
mā	女＋马	妈					
gē	可＋可	哥					

3 为下列汉字标注拼音，并在括号里写出笔画数。

Give the *pinyin* of the following characters and write the stroke numbers in the parentheses.

（1）呢＿＿＿（　　）   （4）哥＿＿＿（　　）

（2）吗＿＿＿（　　）   （5）林＿＿＿（　　）

（3）妈＿＿＿（　　）

4 为每个汉字标注拼音，并找到与它相应的图片，然后连线。

Give the *pinyin* of the following characters and find the corresponding drawings. Draw a line to connect the two.

（1）丁

（2）刀

（3）口

5 不看课本，尽量写出本课出现的汉字。

Write as many characters as you can from this lesson without reading the textbook.

_____

_____

_____

她是哪国人

一　汉字学习　Learning Chinese Characters

1 认写基本汉字　Learn and write basic Chinese characters

(1)　人　　　丿 人

rén　　　　people, person　　　　　　　2 strokes

Note: On the left side of a character, "人" is written as "亻".

(2)　十　　　一 十

shí　　　　ten　　　　　　　　　　　　2 strokes

(3)　匕　　　丿 匕

bǐ　　　　dagger　　　　　　　　　　　2 strokes

(4)　中　　　丨 冂 口 中

zhōng　　　middle　　　　　　　　　　　4 strokes

(5)　日　　　丨 冂 日 日

rì　　　　sun　　　　　　　　　　　　4 strokes

(6)　贝（貝）　丨 冂 贝 贝

bèi　　　　shell　　　　　　　　　　　　4 strokes

(7) 玉 　　一 二 干 王 玉

yù　　jade　　　　　　　　　　　　　　5 strokes

Note: On the left side of the character, "玉" is written as "王".

(8) 矢 　　丿 ㇇ ㇒ 午 矢

shǐ　　arrow　　　　　　　　　　　　5 strokes

(9) 生 　　丿 ㇒ 十 牛 生

shēng　　to be born; *a suffix denoting person*　　5 strokes

(10) 者 　　一 十 土 耂 者 者 者 者

zhě　　person, thing　　　　　　　　　8 strokes

2 认写课文中的汉字 Learn and write the Chinese characters in the text

(1) 她 tā

她 ⟶ 女 + 也　　　　　　　　　　6 strokes

(The "female" side "女" denotes something related to a woman.)

(2) 他 tā

他 ⟶ 亻 + 也　　　　　　　　　　5 strokes

(The "standing person" side "亻" denotes something related to a person.)

(3) 们 men (們)

们 ⟶ 亻 + 门　　　　　　　　　　5 strokes

(The meaning side is "亻", and the phonetic side is "门".)

(4) 你 nǐ

你 ⟶ 亻 + 尔 (尔: 丿 ㇇ 午 尓 尔)　　7 strokes

(The "standing person" side "亻" denotes something related to a person.)

阝 (yòu'ěrdāor, the "right-ear" side)   ㇌ 阝   2 strokes

𰀁 (nàzìpángr, the side of "那(nà, that)")   𠃌 ㇕ 彐 𰀁   4 strokes

(5) 那 nà

那 —→ 𰀁 + 阝   6 strokes

(6) 哪 nǎ

哪 —→ 口 + 那   9 strokes

(The meaning side is " 口 ", and the phonetic side is "那".)

(7) 娜 nà

娜 —→ 女 + 那   9 strokes

(The meaning side is " 女 ", and the phonetic side is "那".)

耂 (lǎozìtóur, the top of "老(lǎo, old)")   一 十 土 耂   4 strokes

巾 (jīnzìr, the character "巾(jīn, towel)")   丨 冂 巾   3 strokes

丿 (shīzìpángr, the side of "师(shī, teacher)")   丨 丿   2 strokes

(8) 都 dōu

都 —→ 者 + 阝   10 strokes

(9) 老师 lǎoshī （老師）

老 —→ 耂 + 匕   6 strokes

师 —→ 丿 + 一 + 巾   6 strokes

口 (guózìkuàngr, the frame of "国(guó, country)" denotes the boundary of a country.)

丨 冂 口   3 strokes

(10) 中国 Zhōngguó （中國）

国 —→ 口 + 玉   8 strokes

匚 (qūzìkuàngr, the frame of "区(qū, district)")   一 匚   2 strokes

（11）医生 yīshēng（醫生）

医 → 匚 ＋ 矢 （一 丁 丆 匸 窂 医 医） 7 strokes

（12）是 shì

是 → 日 ＋ 疋 9 strokes

二 书写练习 Writing Exercises

1 按正确的笔顺描汉字，并在后边的空格里写汉字。

Trace over the characters, following the correct stroke order. Then copy the characters in the blank spaces.

人	丿 人	人	人					
十	一 十	十	十					
匕	丿 匕	匕	匕					
中	丨 冂 口 中	中	中					
日	丨 冂 冃 日	日	日					
贝	丨 冂 贝 贝	贝	贝					
玉	一 二 干 王 玉	玉	玉					
矢	丿 𠂉 二 午 矢	矢	矢					
生	丿 𠂉 二 牛 生	生	生					
者	一 十 土 耂 者 者 者	者	者					

2 在空格里写汉字，注意汉字的部件。

Write the characters in the blank spaces, paying attention to the character components.

tā	女 + 也	她						
tā	亻 + 也	他						
men	亻 + 门	们						
nǐ	亻 + 尔	你						
nà	彐 + 阝	那						
nǎ	口 + 那	哪						
nà	女 + 那	娜						
dōu	者 + 阝	都						
lǎo	耂 + 匕	老						
shī	丿 + 帀	师						
guó	囗 + 玉	国						
yī	匚 + 矢	医						
shì	日 + 疋	是						

3 为下列汉字标注拼音，并在括号里写出笔画数。

Give the *pinyin* of the following characters and write the stroke numbers in the parentheses.

（1）哪＿＿＿＿（　　　）　　（4）师＿＿＿＿（　　　）

（2）国＿＿＿＿（　　　）　　（5）医＿＿＿＿（　　　）

（3）老＿＿＿＿（　　　）　　（6）生＿＿＿＿（　　　）

4 根据所给拼音，在第二行汉字中找到能与第一行汉字组成词语的汉字，然后连线。

Find a character in the second line which can be combined with a character in the first line to make a word according to the *pinyin* provided. Draw a line to connect the two.

（1）wàiyǔ　　（2）lǎoshī　　（3）yīshēng　　（4）Zhōngguó　　（5）tāmen

他　　　　老　　　　中　　　　医　　　　外

生　　　　们　　　　语　　　　国　　　　师

5 不看课本，尽量写出本课出现的汉字。

Write as many characters as you can from this lesson without reading the textbook.

_____

_____

_____

认识你很高兴

一　汉字学习　Learning Chinese Characters

1 笔顺规则　Rules of stroke order

Example	Stroke Order	Rule to Write
十	一 十	Horizontal before vertical
人	丿 人	Left-falling before right-falling
妈	女 妈	From left to right
只	口 只	From top to bottom
月	刀 月	From outside to inside
国	冂 囯 国	Outside before inside and inside before enclosing
小	亅 小 小	Middle before two sides

2 认写基本汉字　Learn and write basic Chinese characters

(1) 七　一 七

qī　　seven　　　　　　　　2 strokes

(2) 小　丨小小
xiǎo　　small, little　　　　　3 strokes

(3) 心　丶心心心
xīn　　heart　　　　　4 strokes

Note: On the left side of a character, "心" is written as "忄", as in "忙 (máng)".

(4) 水　丨冫水水
shuǐ　　water　　　　　4 strokes

Note: On the left side of a character, "水" is written as "氵", as in "汉 (hàn)".

(5) 月　丿刀月月
yuè　　moon　　　　　4 strokes

(6) 手　一二三手
shǒu　　hand　　　　　4 strokes

Note: On the left side of a character, "手" is written as "扌".

(7) 田　丨冂冂田田
tián　　field　　　　　5 strokes

(8) 白　丿亻白白白
bái　　white　　　　　5 strokes

(9) 只　丶口口尸只
zhǐ　　only　　　　　5 strokes

(10) 言　丶亠亖言言言言
yán　　speech　　　　　7 strokes

Note: On the left side of a character, "言" is written as "讠", as in "认识 (rènshi)".

17

3 认写课文中的汉字　Learn and write the Chinese characters in the text

(1) 认识 rènshi（認識）

认 → 讠 + 人　　　　　　　　4 strokes

（"讠", the meaning side denotes language-related behavior.）

识 → 讠 + 只　　　　　　　　7 strokes

（The meaning side "讠" plus the phonetic side "只 (zhǐ)".）

(2) 语言 yǔyán（語言）

语 → 讠 + 五 + 口　　　　　　9 strokes

讠 (sāndiǎnshuǐr, the side of "three-drops-of-water") 丶丶讠　3 strokes

(3) 汉语 Hànyǔ（漢語）

汉 → 氵 + 又　　　　　　　　5 strokes

(4) 您 nín

您 → 你 + 心　　　　　　　　11 strokes

ナ (yǒuzìtóur, the top of "有(yǒu, to have)") 一 ナ　2 strokes

(5) 朋友 péngyou

朋 → 月 + 月　　　　　　　　8 strokes

友 → ナ + 又　　　　　　　　4 strokes

(6) 贵姓 guìxìng（貴姓）

贵 → 虫 + 一 + 贝　　　　　9 strokes

姓 → 女 + 生　　　　　　　　8 strokes

(7) 叫 jiào

叫 → 口 + 丩　　　　　　　　5 strokes

（8）的 de

的 → 白 ＋ 勺   8 strokes

二　书写练习　Writing Exercises

1 按正确的笔顺描汉字，并在后边的空格里写汉字。

Trace over the characters, following the correct stroke order. Then copy the characters in the blank spaces.

七	一 七	七	七				
小	丿 小 小	小	小				
心	丶 心 心 心	心	心				
水	丨 刁 才 水	水	水				
月	丿 几 月 月	月	月				
手	丿 二 三 手	手	手				
田	丨 冂 日 田 田	田	田				
白	丿 亻 白 白 白	白	白				
只	丶 口 口 尸 只	只	只				
言	丶 二 亖 言 言 言	言	言				

2 在空格里写汉字，注意汉字的部件。

Write the characters in the blank spaces, paying attention to the character components.

rèn	讠 ＋ 人	认							

shí	讠 + 只	识						
yǔ	讠 + 五 + 口	语						
hàn	氵 + 又	汉						
nín	你 + 心	您						
péng	月 + 月	朋						
yǒu	𠂇 + 又	友						
guì	中 + 一 + 贝	贵						
xìng	女 + 生	姓						
jiào	口 + 丩	叫						
de	白 + 勺	的						

3 为下列汉字标注拼音，并在括号里写出笔画数。

Give the *pinyin* of the following characters and write the stroke numbers in the parentheses.

（1）识_____（   ）   （4）您_____（   ）

（2）语_____（   ）   （5）贵_____（   ）

（3）水_____（   ）

4 根据所给拼音，在第二行汉字中找到能与第一行汉字组成词语的汉字，然后连线。

Find a character in the second line which can be combined with a character in the first line to make a word according to the *pinyin* provided. Draw a line to connect the two.

（1）Hànyǔ   （2）péngyou   （3）guìxìng   （4）rènshi   （5）xuésheng

　　　　学　　　　　　朋　　　　　　汉　　　　　　贵　　　　　　认

　　　　识　　　　　　姓　　　　　　生　　　　　　友　　　　　　语

5 不看课本，尽量写出本课出现的汉字。

Write as many characters as you can from this lesson without reading the textbook.

_____

_____

_____

餐厅在哪儿

一 汉字学习 Learning Chinese Characters

1 汉字复合笔画（1） Combined character strokes (1)

Stroke	Name	Example	Way to Write
⁻	hénggōu	你	The horizontal stroke with a hook, is written like the fourth stroke in "你".
コ	héngzhé	马	The horizontal stroke with a downward turn, is written like the first stroke in "马".
フ	héngpiě	又	The horizontal stroke with a downward turn to the left, is written like the first stroke in "又".
コ	héngzhégōu	门	The horizontal stroke with a downward turn and a hook, is written like the third stroke in "门".
㇛	héngzhétí	语	The horizontal stroke with a downward turn，and then an upward turn to the right, is written like the second stroke in "语".
亅	shùgōu	丁	The vertical stroke with a hook, is written like the second stroke in "丁".

2 认写基本汉字 Learn and write basic Chinese characters

(1) 二   一 二

èr   two   2 strokes

(2) 儿（兒）　丿儿

ér　　son　　2 strokes

(3) 子　　乛了子

zǐ　　son　　3 strokes

(4) 井　　一二井井

jǐng　　well　　4 strokes

(5) 文　　丶一ナ文

wén　　written language　　4 strokes

(6) 见（見）　丨冂贝见

jiàn　　to see　　4 strokes

(7) 且　　丨冂月且且

qiě　　and　　5 strokes

Note: "且" is the original character for "祖(zǔ, ancestor)". When it became a loaned function word, "祖" substitutes for the original character.

(8) 四　　丨冂四四四

sì　　four　　5 strokes

(9) 我　　一二于手我我我

wǒ　　I, me　　7 strokes

(10) 青　　一二キ主青青青

qīng　　blue, green　　8 strokes

实用汉语课本 入门级 汉字册

3 认写课文中的汉字　Learn and write the Chinese characters in the text

犬（zàizìtóur, the top of "在(zài, to be (in, on, at))"）　　3 strokes

一ナ犬

(1) 在 zài

在 → 犬 + 土　　6 strokes

(2) 坐 zuò

坐 → 人 + 人 + 土　　7 strokes

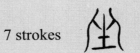

(3) 请问 qǐngwèn（請問）

请 → 讠 + 青　　10 strokes

(The meaning side is "讠", and the phonetic side is "青(qīng)".)

问 → 门 + 口　　6 strokes

辶 (zǒuzhīr, the bottom of "walking")　` 讠 辶　　3 strokes

(4) 这 zhè（這）

这 → 文 + 辶　　7 strokes

(5) 进 jìn（進）

进 → 井 + 辶　　7 strokes

(6) 再见 zàijiàn（再見）

再 → 一 + 冂 + 土　　6 strokes

（一 丆 丙 再 再）

丷 (xuézìtóur, the top of "学(xué, to study)")

` 丷 丷 丷 丷　　5 strokes

(7) 学生 xuésheng（學生）

学 → 丷 + 子　　8 strokes

24

（8）好 hǎo

好 → 女 + 子　　　　　　　6 strokes

（9）小姐 xiǎojie

姐 → 女 + 且　　　　　　　8 strokes

冂 (zhōuzìkuàngr, the frame of "周(zhōu, border)")

丿 冂　　　　　　　2 strokes

（10）不用 búyòng

用 → 冂 + ≢　　　　　　　5 strokes

二　书写练习　Writing Exercises

1 按正确的笔顺描汉字，并在后边的空格里写汉字。

Trace over the characters, following the correct stroke order. Then copy the characters in the blank spaces.

二	一 二	二	二				
儿	丿 儿	儿	儿				
子	乛 了 子	子	子				
井	一 二 丰 井	井	井				
文	丶 一 ナ 文	文	文				
见	丨 冂 贝 见	见	见				
且	丨 冂 日 日 且	且	且				
四	丨 冂 卬 四 四	四	四				

| 我 | 一 二 于 于 我 我 我 | 我 | 我 | | | | | | |
| 青 | 一 二 丰 丰 青 青 青 | 青 | 青 | | | | | | |

2 在空格里写汉字，注意汉字的部件。

Write the characters in the blank spaces, paying attention to the character components.

zài	才 + 土	在							
zuò	人 + 人 + 土	坐							
qǐng	讠 + 青	请							
wèn	门 + 口	问							
zhè	文 + 辶	这							
jìn	井 + 辶	进							
zài	一 + 冂 + 土	再							
xué	学 + 子	学							
hǎo	女 + 子	好							
jiě	女 + 且	姐							
yòng	冂 + 扌	用							

3 为下列汉字标注拼音，并在括号里写出笔画数。

Give the *pinyin* of the following characters and write the stroke numbers in the parentheses.

（1）坐＿＿＿＿（　　　）　　　　　（2）谢＿＿＿＿（　　　）

26

（3）请_____（　　　） 　　　　　（5）姐_____（　　　）

（4）学_____（　　　）

4 根据所给拼音，在第二行汉字中找到能与第一行汉字组成词语的汉字，然后连线。

Find a character in the second line which can be combined with a character in the first line to make a word according to the *pinyin* provided. Draw a line to connect the two.

（1）zàijiàn 　　（2）qǐngwèn 　　（3）xiǎojie 　　（4）cāntīng 　　（5）zhīdao

请　　　　再　　　　小　　　　知　　　　餐

厅　　　　姐　　　　问　　　　见　　　　道

5 不看课本，尽量写出本课出现的汉字。

Write as many characters as you can from this lesson without reading the textbook.

_____

_____

_____

我们去游泳，好吗

一 汉字学习 Learning Chinese Characters

1 汉字复合笔画（2） Combined character strokes (2)

Stroke	Name	Example	Way to Write
ㄴ	shùzhé	山	The vertical stroke with a horizontal turn to the right, is written like the second stroke in "山".
レ	shùtí	以	The vertical stroke with an upward turn to the right, is written like the first stroke in "以".
𠃌	shùzhézhé-gōu	马	The vertical stroke with a horizontal turn to the right, and then a downward turn and a hook, is written like the second stroke in "马".
乀	héngzhé-wāngōu	九	The horizontal stroke with a downward turn to the left, and then a horizontal turn to the right and an upward hook, is written like the second stroke in "九".
ㄥ	piězhé	么	The downward stroke to the left, and then a horizontal turn to the right, is written like the second stroke in "么".
〱	piědiǎn	女	The downward stroke to the left and then an extended dot to the right, is written like the first stroke in "女".

2 笔画组合　Combination of strokes

The relationship between strokes in a Chinese character can be essential to its meaning. There are three ways to combine strokes in a character.

(1) Adjacent (not attached) like "八", "儿", "二", "小";

(2) Crossing like "十", "大", "九", "夫";

(3) Connecting like "厂", "丁", "人", "山", "天".

3 认写基本汉字　Learn and write basic Chinese characters

(1) 九　　　丿九

jiǔ　　　nine　　　　　　　2 strokes

(2) 厶　　　厶 厶

sī　　　private　　　　　　2 strokes

Note: "厶" is the variant form of "私 (sī)". "私" is frequently used now.

(3) 寸　　　一 寸 寸

cùn　　　*(a traditional unit of length,*
　　　　　1 cun equals 1/30 meter)　3 strokes

(4) 工　　　一 丁 工

gōng　　　labor　　　　　　3 strokes

(5) 亡　　　丶 亠 亡

wáng　　　to die　　　　　　3 strokes

(6) 三　　　一 二 三

sān　　　three　　　　　　3 strokes

(7) 气（氣）　　　丿 𠂉 气 气

qì　　　air　　　　　　4 strokes

(8) 立　　　丶 ﹁ 亠 立 立

lì　　　　to stand　　　　5 strokes

(9) 身　　　丿 亻 竹 白 白 身 身

shēn　　　body　　　　7 strokes

Note: On the left side or in the middle of a character, "身" is written as "身".

(10) 兑　　　丶 丷 丷 兯 兯 户 兑

duì　　　to exchange　　　7 strokes

4 认写课文中的汉字　Learn and write the Chinese characters in the text

(1) 去 qù

去 → 土 ＋ 厶　　　　5 strokes

(2) 有意思 yǒu yìsi

有 → 𠂇 ＋ 月　　　　6 strokes

意 → 立 ＋ 曰 ＋ 心　　　13 strokes

思（sī）→ 田 ＋ 心　　　9 strokes

(3) 天气 tiānqì（天氣）

天 → 一 ＋ 大　　　　4 strokes

(4) 太 tài

太 → 大 ＋ 丶　　　　4 strokes

(5) 什么 shénme（什麼）

什 → 亻 ＋ 十　　　　4 strokes

么 → 丿 ＋ 厶　　　　3 strokes

(6) 时候 shíhou （時候）

时 → 日 + 寸　　　　　　　　　　7 strokes

（The side of "日" denotes time.）

候（hòu）→ 亻 + ∣ + ⼆ + 矢　　10 strokes

（ノ 亻 亻 伫 伫 伫 侯 侯 候 ）

(7) 现在 xiànzài （現在）

现 → 王 + 见　　　　　　　　　　8 strokes

(8) 明天 míngtiān

明 → 日 + 月　　　　　　　　　　8 strokes

（The side of "日" and the side of "月" denote light.）

(9) 时间 shíjiān （時間）

间 → 门 + 日　　　　　　　　　　7 strokes

(10) 说 shuō （説）

说 → 讠 + 兑　　　　　　　　　　9 strokes

忄 （shùxīnpángr, the side of "standing heart"）

、 ⺖ 忄　　　　　　　　　　　　3 strokes

（On the left side of a character, "心" is written as "忄".）

(11) 忙 máng

忙 → 忄 + 亡　　　　　　　　　　6 strokes

(12) 谢谢 xièxie （謝謝）

谢 → 讠 + 身 + 寸　　　　　　　12 strokes

二 书写练习 Writing Exercises

1 按正确的笔顺描汉字，并在后边的空格里写汉字。

Trace over the characters, following the correct stroke order. Then copy the characters in the blank spaces.

九	丿九	九	九					
厶	乙厶	厶	厶					
寸	一寸寸	寸	寸					
工	一丁工	工	工					
亡	丶亠亡	亡	亡					
三	一二三	三	三					
气	丿丆气气	气	气					
立	丶丶亠立立	立	立					
身	丿𠂆𠂉自身身身	身	身					
兑	丶丷丷台兑兑兑	兑	兑					

2 在空格里写汉字，注意汉字的部件。

Write the characters in the blank spaces, paying attention to the character components.

qù	土 + 厶	去						
yǒu	𠂇 + 月	有						
yì	立 + 日 + 心	意						

sī	田 + 心	思							
tiān	一 + 大	天							
tài	大 + 、	太							
shén	亻 + 十	什							
me	丿 + 厶	么							
shí	日 + 寸	时							
hòu	亻 + 丨 + 二 + 矢	候							
xiàn	王 + 见	现							
míng	日 + 月	明							
jiān	门 + 日	间							
shuō	讠 + 兑	说							
máng	忄 + 亡	忙							
xiè	讠 + 身 + 寸	谢							

3 根据所给拼音，在第二行汉字中找到能与第一行汉字组成词语的汉字，然后连线。

Find a character in the second line which can be combined with a character in the first line to make a word according to the *pinyin* provided. Draw a line to connect the two.

（1）míngtiān　　（2）yóuyǒng　　（3）shíjiān　　（4）xiànzài　　（5）jīngjù

京　　　时　　　明　　　游　　　现

天　　　在　　　剧　　　间　　　泳

4 不看课本，尽量写出本课出现的汉字。

Write as many characters as you can from this lesson without reading the textbook.

_____

_____

_____

你认识不认识他

一　汉字学习　Learning Chinese Characters

1 汉字的部件　Chinese character components

There are three aspects as to the structure of a Chinese character: the strokes, the components and the whole character. For example, the character "木" consists of four strokes: "一", "丨", "丿", "丶". It is a basic character and is also used as a component for some other characters. For example, "林" consists of two "木" characters. The components are the core structure of a Chinese character. Chinese characters can be divided into character-parts and non-character-parts. For example, "院" can be divided into the following three parts: "阝", "宀" and "元", of which "元" is a character-part, while "阝" and "宀" are the non-character-parts. The key to learning Chinese characters well is to master their components.

2 认写基本汉字　Learn and write basic Chinese characters

(1) 开（開）　一 二 开 开

kāi　　　to open　　　4 strokes

Note: "开" looks like the bar or the bolt of a door; when the "二" in "开" is removed, the door opens.

(2) 目　丨 冂 冂 月 目

mù　　　eye　　　5 strokes

35

(3) 下　　一丁下　　　　　xià　　below, down　　　　3 strokes

Note: In contrast with "上", the "卜" under "一" denotes "bottom" or "beneath".

(4) 元　　一二于元　　　　yuán　　first, primary　　　4 strokes

(5) 片　　丿丿丿片　　　　piàn　　flat, thin piece; slice　4 strokes

(6) 皮　　一厂户皮皮　　　pí　　skin　　　　　　5 strokes

(7) 弓　　一コ弓　　　　　gōng　　bow　　　　　3 strokes

(8) 长（長）　丿一长长　　zhǎng　to grow　　　　4 strokes

(9) 来（來）　一丶口四平来来　lái　to come　　　7 strokes

(10) 介　　丿人个介　　　jiè　to be situated between, to interpose　4 strokes

(11) 父　　丶丷分父　　　fù　father　　　　　4 strokes

(12) 巴　　　　　フ 刀 刀 巴

bā　　　　　to wait anxiously, to cling to;

　　　　　　a *suffix*　　　　　　4 strokes

Note: "巴" stands on the right side or at the bottom of a Chinese character, and
denotes the pronunciation of the character.

(13) 习（習）　　ㄱ ㄐ 习

xí　　　　　to study　　　　　　3 strokes

(14) 专（專）　　一 二 专 专

zhuān　　　special　　　　　　4 strokes

Note that the third stroke of "专" is one stroke, not two strokes.

(15) 业（業）　　丨 丨丨 丬丨 业 业

yè　　　　　business, trade　　　5 strokes

(16) 羊　　　　　丶 丷 丷 兰 兰 羊

yáng　　　　sheep　　　　　　6 strokes

(17) 术（術）　　一 十 才 木 术

shù　　　　　art, skill　　　　　5 strokes

Note that "术" has one more dot than "木".

(18) 系　　　　　一 丆 幺 幺 系 系 系

xì　　　　　department, system　7 strokes

(19) 为（爲）　　丶 丿 为 为

wéi　　　　　to act, to do　　　　4 strokes

3 认写课文中的汉字　Learn and write the Chinese characters in the text

彳 (shuāngrénpángr, "亻" is called the "single-standing-person" side, "彳" is called the "double-standing-person" side.)　ノ ク 彳　　3 strokes

艮 gèn 　フ ヨ ヨ 日 日 艮　　6 strokes

(1) 很 hěn

很 ⟶ 彳 + 艮　　9 strokes

亠 (jīngzìtóur, the top of "京(jīng, capital)")　丶 亠　　2 strokes

(2) 高兴 gāoxìng（高興）

高 ⟶ 亠 + 口 + 冂 + 口　　10 strokes

兴 ⟶ ⺌ + 一 + 八　　6 strokes

手 (kànzìtóur, the top of "看(kàn, to look)", in a multi-component character, the vertical stroke with a hook "亅" in "手" is written as a downward stroke to the left "ノ".)

一 二 三 手　　4 strokes

(3) 看 kàn

看 ⟶ 手 + 目　　9 strokes

(Hold a hand "手" above one's eyes "目" to gaze.)

阝 (zuǒ'ěrdāor, the side of "left-ear")　⻖ 阝　　2 strokes

(4) 学院 xuéyuàn（學院）

院 ⟶ 阝 + 宀 + 元　　9 strokes

(5) 名片 míngpiàn

名 ⟶ 夕 + 口　　6 strokes

(6) 啊 à

啊 ⟶ 口 + 阝 + 可　　10 strokes

子 (zǐzìpángr, the side of "子(zǐ, son)") フ 了 子   3 strokes

(The horizontal stroke in the character "子" is written as an upward stroke, when the character becomes the left side component of another character.)

攵 (fǎnwénpángr, the side of reversed "文 (wén, originally meant tapping)")

丿 ㇀ 攵 攵   4 strokes

(The dot in "文" is written as "丿", a downward stroke to the left, when the character becomes the right side component of another character.)

爫 (zhǎozìtóur, the top of "爪(zhǎo, claw)") 丿 ㇇ ㇇ 爫   4 strokes

冖 (tūbǎogàir, the top of "bald cover") 丶 冖   2 strokes

(7) 教授 jiàoshòu

教 → 耂 + 子 + 攵   11 strokes

授 → 扌 + 爫 + 冖 + 又   11 strokes

(8) 丁力波 Dīng Lìbō

波 → 氵 + 皮   8 strokes

(9) 张 zhāng (張)

张 → 弓 + 长   7 strokes

(The meaning side is "弓 (gōng)", and the phonetic side is "长 (cháng)".)

隹 zhuī 丿 亻 亻 亻 亻 亻 隹 隹   8 strokes

(10) 谁 shéi (誰)

谁 → 讠 + 隹   10 strokes

纟 (糹) (jiǎosīpángr, the side of "entangled silk") ㇛ 纟 纟   3 strokes

(11) 介绍 jièshào (介紹)

绍 → 纟 + 刀 + 口   8 strokes

宀 (bǎogàir, the top of "roof") 丶 丷 宀   3 strokes

(12) 名字 míngzi

字 → 宀 + 子　　　　　　　　6 strokes

(13) .爸爸 bàba

爸 → 父 + 巴　　　　　　　　8 strokes

("父 (fù)" suggests the meaning and "巴 (bā)" denotes the pronunciation.)

丷 (měizìtóur, the top of "美 (měi, beautiful)")　ˋ ˇ ⺍ ⺍ ⺷ 丷　6 strokes

(14) 美术 měishù（美術）

美 → 丷 + 大　　　　　　　　9 strokes

(15) 加拿大 Jiānádà

加 → 力 + 口　　　　　　　　5 strokes

拿 → 人 + 一 + 丶 + 口 + 手　　10 strokes

(Hands are joined together to denote the meaning of "taking".)

二 书写练习 Writing Exercises

1 按正确的笔顺描汉字，并在后边的空格里写汉字。

Trace over the characters, following the correct stroke order. Then copy the characters in the blank spaces.

开	一 二 开 开	开	开				
目	l 冂 月 月 目	目	目				
下	一 丁 下	下	下				
元	一 二 テ 元	元	元				
片	ノ 丿 广 片	片	片				

皮	ノ ノ 厂 皮 皮	皮	皮					
弓	フ コ 弓	弓	弓					
长	ノ 匕 长 长	长	长					
来	一 亠 口 辺 半 来 来	来	来					
介	ノ 人 介 介	介	介					
父	ノ ハ グ 父	父	父					
巴	フ フ 口 巴	巴	巴					
习	フ 习 习	习	习					
专	一 二 专 专	专	专					
业	丨 刂 刂 业 业	业	业					
羊	` `` 兰 兰 羊	羊	羊					
术	一 十 才 木 术	术	术					
系	一 丂 至 玄 系 系 系	系	系					
为	` ノ 为 为	为	为					

2 在空格里写汉字，注意汉字的部件。

Write the characters in the blank spaces, paying attention to the character components.

| hěn | 彳 + 艮 | 很 | | | | | | |
| gāo | 亠 + 口 + 冂 + 口 | 高 | | | | | | |

xìng	⿱丷一+八	兴							
kàn	手+目	看							
yuàn	阝+宀+元	院							
míng	夕+口	名							
à	口+阝+可	啊							
jiào	耂+子+攵	教							
shòu	扌+⺤+冖+又	授							
bō	氵+皮	波							
zhāng	弓+长	张							
shéi	讠+隹	谁							
shào	纟+刀+口	绍							
zì	宀+子	字							
bà	父+巴	爸							
měi	羊+大	美							
jiā	力+口	加							
ná	人+⺀+口+手	拿							

3 为下列汉字标注拼音，并把它们分解为部件。

Write *pinyin* for the following characters and devide them into character components.

E.g. 剧 _jù_ → _尸 + 古 + 刂_

（1）姓_____ → _____   （2）语_____ → _____

42

（3）师＿＿＿＿→＿＿＿＿＿＿　　　（7）妈＿＿＿＿→＿＿＿＿＿＿

（4）汉＿＿＿＿→＿＿＿＿＿＿　　　（8）那＿＿＿＿→＿＿＿＿＿＿

（5）们＿＿＿＿→＿＿＿＿＿＿　　　（9）都＿＿＿＿→＿＿＿＿＿＿

（6）请＿＿＿＿→＿＿＿＿＿＿　　　（10）的＿＿＿＿→＿＿＿＿＿＿

4 根据所给拼音，在第二行汉字中找到能与第一行汉字组成词语的汉字，然后连线。

Find a character in the second line which can be combined with a character in the first line to make a word according to the *pinyin* provided. Draw a line to connect the two.

（1）kāixué　　（2）xìngmíng　　（3）zhuānyè　　（4）yīyuàn　　（5）Zhōngguó

医　　　　　姓　　　　　专　　　　　开　　　　　中

名　　　　　业　　　　　院　　　　　国　　　　　学

5 猜字谜。

Character riddle.

人有"他"大，

天没"他"大。

请问"他"是谁？

你也认识"他"。

（ The key is a character. ）

6 用学过的汉字描述你的一个朋友。（不少于20个字）

Use the characters you have learned to describe one of your friends (more than 20 characters).

＿＿＿＿＿＿＿＿＿＿＿＿＿＿＿＿＿＿＿＿＿＿＿＿＿＿＿＿＿＿＿＿＿＿＿＿＿＿

＿＿＿＿＿＿＿＿＿＿＿＿＿＿＿＿＿＿＿＿＿＿＿＿＿＿＿＿＿＿＿＿＿＿＿＿＿＿

7 找句子。

Seek and find.

Try to find as many sentences or questions as possible from the following list of characters. Look horizontally and diagonally. Circle each sentence or question and copy it. For example:

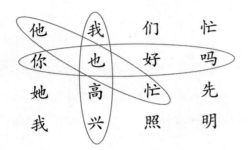

① 他也忙。

② 你也好吗?

③ 我也高兴。

（1）
我	认	识	他
介	学	你	听
绍	说	汉	德
一	写	法	语
下	说	英	文

（2）
他	学	美	术
学	法	律	师
经	画	汽	车
济	家	油	子

你们家有几口人

一 汉字学习 Learning Chinese Characters

1 汉字的结构(1) Structure of Chinese characters (1)

Structurally speaking, Chinese characters fall into two categories: the single-component characters and the multi-component characters. All of the basic Chinese characters we have learned so far are single-component characters, such as "人", "手", "刀", "马", "牛", "羊", "日", "月", "水", "木", "上", "下". The multi-component characters consist of two or more components, such as "爸", "妈", "你", "们", "哪", "语". The order of writing components in a character is similar to the order of writing the strokes of a character. There are three basic types of configuration for multi-component characters:

The left-right structure ①

a. Equal left-right (the numbers indicate the order of writing the components)

| 1 | 2 | 朋 |

b. Small left-big right

| 1 | 2 | 汉 | | 1 | 2 / 3 | 语 |

c. Big left-small right

| 1 | 2 | 那 | | 1 / 2 | 3 | 都 |

2 认写基本汉字 Learn and write basic Chinese characters

(1) 几(幾)   丿 几

jǐ   how many   2 strokes

45

(2) 禾　　　一 二 千 禾 禾

hé　　　standing grain　　　5 strokes

(3) 个（個）　　ノ 人 个

gè　　　(*a measure word*)　　3 strokes

(4) 两（兩）　一 丆 两 丙 丙 两 两

liǎng　　two　　　7 strokes

(5) 未　　　一 二 十 丰 未

wèi　　　not yet　　　5 strokes

(6) 犬　　　一 ナ 大 犬

quǎn　　dog　　　4 strokes

(7) 云（雲）　一 二 云 云

yún　　　cloud　　　4 strokes

(8) 少　　　丨 刂 小 少

shǎo　　few, less　　4 strokes

(9) 士　　　一 十 士

shì　　　person　　3 strokes

(10) 欠　　　ノ 𠂉 𠂉 欠

qiàn　　to owe　　4 strokes

(11) 夕　　　ノ 勹 夕

xī　　　evening　　3 strokes

(12) 卜　　　丨 卜

bǔ　　　divination　　2 strokes

(13) 百   一 丆 丆 百 百 百

bǎi   hundred   6 strokes

3 认写课文中的汉字   Learn and write the Chinese characters in the text

豕 shǐ 一 丆 豕 豕 豕 豕 豕   7 strokes

(1) 家 jiā

家 → 宀 + 豕   10 strokes

(The top of "roof", "宀", denotes a hut. A hut with a pig represents a house. The character "家" reflects the historical change in production mode of the ancient Chinese from hunting to animal husbandry.)

灬 (sìdiǎnr, the character "火" is written as "灬" at the bottom of a multi-component character, and is called the "four-dots" bottom.)

灬 灬 灬 灬   4 strokes

(2) 照片 zhàopiàn

照 → 日 + 刀 + 口 + 灬   13 strokes

(The meaning part is "日" and the phonetic part is "召" (zhào).)

(3) 和 hé

和 → 禾 + 口   8 strokes

丷 (dàobā, the top of "upside down eight") 丶 丷   2 strokes

(4) 弟弟 dìdi

弟 → 丷 + 弔 (弔: 一 コ 弓 弔 弔)   7 strokes

(5) 一共 yígòng

共 → 廿 + 八   6 strokes

(6) 还 hái (還)

还 → 不 + 辶   7 strokes

(7) 妹妹 mèimei

妹 → 女 ＋ 未　　　　　　8 strokes

(The "female" side "女" indicates the character has a feminine connotation.)

犭 (quǎnzìpángr, the side of "犬(quǎn, dog)")　ノ 犭 犭　3 strokes

勹 (bāozìtóur, the top of "包(bāo, to wrap)")　ノ 勹　2 strokes

(8) 狗 gǒu

狗 → 犭 ＋ 勹 ＋ 口　　　　8 strokes

("犬" is the original character for "狗". It is written as "犭" on the left side of characters indicating animals.)

⺌ (shàngzìtóur, the top of "尚(shàng, respecting)")　丨 丷 ⺌　3 strokes

彐 (xuězìdǐr, the bottom of "雪(xuě, snow)")　フ ㇇ 彐　3 strokes

(9) 当然 dāngrán（當然）

当 → ⺌ ＋ 彐　　　　　　6 strokes

然 → 夕 ＋ 犬 ＋ 灬　　　12 strokes

(The combination of a "flesh" side, a "dog" side and a "fire" side, indicating "to roast dog meat over the fire", produces the character, "然", which originally meant "burning". Now this character carries different meanings.)

(10) 真 zhēn

真 → 十 ＋ 且 ＋ 八　　　10 strokes

(11) 可爱 kě'ài（可愛）

爱 → 爫 ＋ 冖 ＋ 友　　　10 strokes

殳 shū　ノ 几 㐅 殳　4 strokes

(12) 没 méi

没 → 氵 ＋ 殳　　　　　　7 strokes

(13) 男 nán

男 → 田 ＋ 力　　　　　　　7 strokes

(14) 做 zuò

做 → 亻＋ 古 ＋ 攵　　　　11 strokes

乍 zhà　ノ 𠂉 仁 乍 乍　　　5 strokes

(15) 工作 gōngzuò

作 → 亻＋ 乍　　　　　　　7 strokes

(16) 多少 duōshao

多 → 夕 ＋ 夕　　　　　　　6 strokes

(17) 喜欢 xǐhuan（喜歡）

喜 → 士 ＋ 口 ＋ ⺌ ＋ 一 ＋ 口　　12 strokes

欢 → 又 ＋ 欠　　　　　　　6 strokes

(On the left side of a multi-component character, the second stroke of "又" is written as an extended dot.)

(18) 外语 wàiyǔ（外語）

外 → 夕 ＋ 卜　　　　　　　5 strokes

二　书写练习　Writing Exercises

1 按正确的笔顺描汉字，并在后边的空格里写汉字。

Trace over the characters, following the correct stroke order. Then copy the characters in the blank spaces.

几	ノ 几		几	几						

49

禾	一 二 千 禾 禾	禾	禾						
个	丿 人 个	个	个						
两	一 丆 币 币 丙 两 两	两	两						
未	一 二 千 未 未	未	未						
犬	一 ナ 大 犬	犬	犬						
云	一 二 云 云	云	云						
少	丨 丨 小 少	少	少						
士	一 十 士	士	士						
欠	丿 𠂊 𠂉 欠	欠	欠						
夕	丿 ㄅ 夕	夕	夕						
卜	丨 卜	卜	卜						
百	一 丆 丆 百 百 百	百	百						

2 在空格里写汉字，注意汉字的部件。

Write the characters in the blank spaces, paying attention to the character components.

jiā	宀 + 豕	家				
zhào	日 + 刀 + 口 + 灬	照				
hé	禾 + 口	和				

dì	⏦ + 弔 + 丿	弟						
gòng	丗 + 八	共						
hái	不 + 辶	还						
mèi	女 + 未	妹						
gǒu	犭 + 勹 + 口	狗						
dāng	灬 + 彐	当						
rán	夕 + 犬 + 灬	然						
zhēn	十 + 且 + 八	真						
ài	爫 + 冖 + 友	爱						
méi	氵 + 殳	没						
nán	田 + 力	男						
zuò	亻 + 古 + 攵	做						
zuò	亻 + 乍	作						
duō	夕 + 夕	多						
xǐ	士 + 口 + 丷 + 一 + 口	喜						
huān	又 + 欠	欢						
wài	夕 + 卜	外						

3 为下列汉字标注拼音，并把它们分解为部件。

Write *pinyin* for the following characters and divide them into character components.

E.g. 谁 _shéi_ → _讠 + 隹_

（1）张_____ → _____   （4）谁_____ → _____

（2）教_____ → _____   （5）请_____ → _____

（3）授_____ → _____   （6）作_____ → _____

4 根据所给拼音，在第二行汉字中找到能与第一行汉字组成词语的汉字，然后连线。

Find a character in the second line which can be combined with a character in the first line to make a word according to the *pinyin* provided. Draw a line to connect the two.

（1）gāoxìng　　（2）jièshào　　（3）xǐhuan　　（4）Hànyǔ　　（5）dāngrán

当　　　　介　　　　汉　　　　喜　　　　高

绍　　　　兴　　　　然　　　　语　　　　欢

5 在汉字"口"的上下左右各加一个部件，组成四个学过的汉字。

Add character components to each side of the character "口" to form four characters which we have learned.

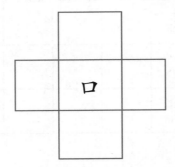

（Key to Exercise 5 in Lesson 7: 一）

6 用学过的汉字描述你的家庭。（不少于50个字）

Use the characters you have learned to describe your family (more than 50 characters).

_____

_____

_____

第九课
Lesson 9

他今年十九岁

一 汉字学习 Learning Chinese Characters

1 汉字的结构(2) Structure of Chinese characters (2)

The left-right structure ②

Equal left-middle-right

1	2	3

谢 娜

2 认写基本汉字 Learn and write basic Chinese characters

(1) 今 ノ 人 仌 今
jīn   today   4 strokes

(2) 年 ノ ㇒ ㇇ ㇌ ㇌ 年
nián   year   6 strokes

(3) 果 丨 冂 冂 日 旦 甲 里 果
guǒ   fruit   8 strokes

(4) 其 一 十 艹 艹 甘 共 其 其
qí   he(his), she(her), it(its),

they(their)   8 strokes

(5) 上　　　丨 卜 上
shàng　　above　　　　　　3 strokes
Note: Placing "卜" on top of "一" means "above".

(6) 午　　　丿 ㇏ 乞 午
wǔ　　noon　　　　　　4 strokes

(7) 出　　　乚 凵 屮 出 出
chū　　to go, to come out　　5 strokes
Note: "凵" denotes a cave, and "屮" denotes one foot stepping out of the cave.

(8) 面（麵）　一 丆 亓 币 而 而 面 面 面
miàn　　noodle　　　　　9 strokes

(9) 尸　　　㇆ 尸 尸
shī　　corpse　　　　　　3 strokes
Note: "尸" denotes a corpse or a carcass.

(10) 了　　　㇇ 了
le　　(a particle)　　　　2 strokes

(11) 虫（蟲）　丶 ㇑ 口 口 中 虫 虫
chóng　　insect, worm　　　6 strokes

(12) 耳　　　一 厂 打 钎 耳 耳
ěr　　ear　　　　　　6 strokes

(13) 乞　　　丿 ㇏ 乞
qǐ　　to beg　　　　　　3 strokes

(14) 米　　　丶 丶 丷 半 米 米
mǐ　　rice　　　　　　6 strokes
Note: The four dots in "米" stand for grains of rice.

(15) 头（頭） 、 ` ゠ 头 头
tóu   head   5 strokes

(16) 瓦   一 厂 瓦 瓦
wǎ   tile   4 strokes

3 认写课文中的汉字 Learn and write the Chinese characters in the text

(1) 岁 suì（歲）
岁 → 山 ＋ 夕   6 strokes

(2) 怎么样 zěnmeyàng（怎麼樣）
怎 → 乍 ＋ 心   9 strokes
样 → 木 ＋ 羊   10 strokes

(3) 课 kè（課）
课 → 讠 ＋ 果   10 strokes

(4) 星期 xīngqī
星 → 日 ＋ 生   9 strokes
期 → 其 ＋ 月   12 strokes

万 (hàozìdǐr, the bottom of "号(hào, number)") 一 万 2 strokes

(5) 号 hào（號）
号 → 口 ＋ 万   5 strokes

(6) 属 shǔ（屬）
属 → 尸 ＋ 一 ＋ 虫 ＋ 冂   12 strokes

乑 (jùzìdǐr, the bottom of "聚(jù, togather)")
一 丁 丁 丅 乑 乑   6 strokes

(7) 聚会 jùhuì（聚會）

聚 → 耳 + 又 + 氺   14 strokes

会 → 人 + 云   6 strokes

礻 (shìzìpángr, the side of "视(shì, manifestation)") 丶 礻 礻 礻 4 strokes

（8）祝贺 zhùhè（祝賀）

祝 → 礻 + 兄   9 strokes

贺 → 力 + 口 + 贝   9 strokes

彡 (sānpiěr, the side of "three-left-falling-stroke") 丿 彡 彡 3 strokes

（9）参加 cānjiā（參加）

参 → 厶 + 大 + 彡   8 strokes

（10）吃 chī

吃 → 口 + 乞   6 strokes

(Use mouth "口" to eat "吃".)

（11）蛋糕 dàngāo

蛋 → 疋 + 虫   11 strokes

糕 → 米 + 羔   16 strokes

(On the left side of a character, the sixth stroke in "米" is written as a dot.)

乛 (hénggōu, a horizontal stroke with a hook) 乛 1 stroke

（12）买 mǎi（買）

买 → 乛 + 头   6 strokes

（13）瓶 píng

瓶 → 丷 + 开 + 瓦   10 strokes

（14）红 hóng（紅）

红 → 纟 + 工   6 strokes

艹 (cǎozìtóur, the top of "草(cǎo, grass)")　一十艹　　　3 strokes

甫 fǔ　一丁丆丆甬甫甫　　　7 strokes

缶 fǒu　ノ乍乍生缶缶　　　6 strokes

(15) 葡萄 pútao

葡 → 艹 + 勹 + 甫　　　12 strokes

萄 (táo) → 艹 + 勹 + 缶　　　11 strokes

酉 yǒu　一丆丆丙西酉酉　　　7 strokes

(16) 酒 jiǔ

酒 → 氵 + 酉　　　10 strokes

(17) 宋华 Sòng Huá (宋華)

宋 → 宀 + 木　　　7 strokes

华 → 化 + 十　　　6 strokes

扌 (běizìpángr, the side of "北(běi, north)")　丨丨扌　　　3 strokes

(18) 北京 Běijīng

北 → 扌 + 匕　　　5 strokes

京 → 亠 + 口 + 小　　　8 strokes

夬 (juézìpángr, the side of "决(jué, decision)")　フ⊐尹夬　　　4 strokes

(19) 快乐 kuàilè (快樂)

快 → 忄 + 夬　　　7 strokes

覀 (xīzìtóur, the top of "西(xī, west)")　一丆丆襾襾襾　　　6 strokes

(20) 漂亮 piàoliang

漂 → 氵 + 覀 + 二 + 小　　　14 strokes

亮 (liàng) → 亠 + 口 + 冖 + 几　　　9 strokes

(21) 烤鸭 kǎoyā（烤鴨）

烤 ⟶ 火 ＋ 耂 ＋ 丂（丂：一 勹）　　　　10 strokes

鸭 ⟶ 甲 ＋ 鸟　　　　　　　　　　　　10 strokes

（甲：丨 冂 日 日 甲；鸟：ノ 勹 勹 乌 鸟）

(22) 喝 hē

喝 ⟶ 口 ＋ 日 ＋ 勹 ＋ 人 ＋ 乚　　　12 strokes

(23) 寿面 shòumiàn（壽麵）

寿 ⟶ 龶 ＋ 寸（龶：一 二 三 丰）　　　7 strokes

二　书写练习　Writing Exercises

1 按正确的笔顺描汉字，并在后边的空格里写汉字。

Trace over the characters, following the correct stroke order. Then copy the characters in the blank spaces.

今	ノ 人 亼 今	今	今						
年	ノ ⺉ 匕 午 生 年	年	年						
果	丨 冂 日 日 旦 甲 里 果	果	果						
其	一 十 廿 甘 甘 苴 其 其	其	其						
上	丨 ⺊ 上	上	上						
午	ノ ⺉ 匕 午	午	午						
出	乚 凵 屮 出 出	出	出						
面	一 丆 丆 襾 而 而 面 面 面	面	面						

尸	フコ尸	尸	尸					
了	フ了	了	了					
虫	丶口口中虫虫	虫	虫					
耳	一丆丌丌耳耳	耳	耳					
乞	丿𠂉乞	乞	乞					
米	丶丷丷半米米	米	米					
头	丶丷二头头	头	头					
瓦	一丆瓦瓦	瓦	瓦					

2 在空格里写汉字，注意汉字的部件。

Write the characters in the blank spaces, paying attention to the character components.

suì	山 + 夕	岁						
zěn	乍 + 心	怎						
yàng	木 + 羊	样						
kè	讠 + 果	课						
xīng	日 + 生	星						
qī	其 + 月	期						
hào	口 + 万	号						
shǔ	尸 + 丶 + 虫 + 冂	属						

jù	耳 + 又 + 水	聚						
huì	人 + 云	会						
zhù	礻 + 兄	祝						
hè	力 + 口 + 贝	贺						
cān	厶 + 大 + 彡	参						
chī	口 + 乞	吃						
dàn	疋 + 虫	蛋						
gāo	米 + 羔	糕						
mǎi	乛 + 头	买						
píng	丷 + 开 + 瓦	瓶						
hóng	纟 + 工	红						
pú	艹 + 勹 + 甫	葡						
táo	艹 + 勹 + 缶	萄						
jiǔ	氵 + 酉	酒						
sòng	宀 + 木	宋						
huá	亻 + 七 + 十	华						
běi	扌 + 匕	北						
jīng	亠 + 口 + 小	京						
kuài	忄 + 夬	快						

pinyin	components	character							
piào	氵＋西＋二＋小	漂							
liàng	亠＋口＋冖＋几	亮							
kǎo	火＋耂＋丂	烤							
yā	甲＋鸟	鸭							
hē	口＋日＋勹＋人＋乚	喝							
shòu	耂＋寸	寿							

3 把下列汉字分解成部件。

Divide the following characters into character components.

（1）哪 → _____ 　　（4）咖 → _____

（2）娜 → _____ 　　（5）啊 → _____

（3）谢 → _____ 　　（6）做 → _____

4 为每个汉字标注拼音，并找到与它相应的图，然后连线。

Give the *pinyin* of the following characters and find the corresponding drawings. Draw a line to connect the two.

（1）耳　　　　　　　　　　　　　　　　

（2）手　　　　　　　　　　　　　　　　

（3）头　　　　　　　　　　　　　　　　

（4）目

（5）人

（6）口

5 根据所给拼音，在第二行汉字中找到能与第一行汉字组成词语的汉字，然后连线。

Find a character in the second line which can be combined with a character in the first line to make a word according to the *pinyin* provided. Draw a line to connect the two.

（1）jùhuì　（2）cānjiā　（3）hóngjiǔ　（4）zhùhè　（5）xǐhuan

参　　　聚　　　红　　　祝　　　喜

贺　　　欢　　　加　　　酒　　　会

6 在汉字"又"的左边和右边各加一个部件，组成两个学过的汉字。

Add character components to each side of the character "又" to form two characters which we have learned.

	又	

（Key to Exercise 5 in Lesson 8: 名、号、加、叫/吗/吃）

7 用学过的汉字描述你自己。（不少于50个字）

Use the characters you have learned to describe yourself (more than 50 characters).

_____

_____

_____

我在这儿买光盘

一 汉字学习　**Learning Chinese Characters**

---

1 汉字的结构（3）　Structure of Chinese characters (3)

The top-bottom structure

a. Equal top-bottom

1
2

男　是

c. Small top-big bottom

1
2

家

1	
2	3

宿

b. Big top-small bottom

1
2

兴

1	2
3	

然

d. Equal top-middle-bottom

1
2
3

意

1	
2	3
4	

照

2 认写基本汉字　Learn and write basic Chinese characters

(1) 舟　　　′ ｊ 丿 刀 舟 舟
zhōu　　　boat　　　　　　　　6 strokes

(2) 皿　　　丶 冂 冂 皿 皿
mǐn　　　household utensils　　5 strokes

(3) 乐（樂）　　一 仁 乐 乐 乐
yuè　　　music　　　　　　　5 strokes

64

(4) 足　　　丶口口早尸足足

zú　　　　foot　　　　　　　　**7 strokes**

(5) 书（書）　　┐ 马 书 书

shū　　　　book　　　　　　　**4 strokes**

(6) 本　　　一 十 才 木 本

běn　　　root of a tree　　　**5 strokes**

Note: The "–" at the bottom of "本" indicates the root.

(7) 平　　　一 丷 口 亚 平

píng　　　flat　　　　　　　**5 strokes**

(8) 走　　　一 十 土 卡 卡 走 走

zǒu　　　to walk　　　　　　**7 strokes**

Note: The ancient character looks like a runner.

(9) 己　　　┐ ヲ 己

jǐ　　　oneself　　　　　　　**3 strokes**

(10) 穴　　　丶 丷 宀 宍 穴

xué　　　cave　　　　　　　**5 strokes**

(11) 勿　　　丿 勹 勹 勿

wù　　　no, not　　　　　　**4 strokes**

(12) 金　　　丿 人 人 今 仐 全 金 金

jīn　　　gold　　　　　　　**8 strokes**

(13) 斤　　　一 厂 斤 斤

jīn　　　(a traditional unit of weight, 1 jin

equals to 0.5 kilograms)　　**4 strokes**

Note: The ancient character resembles an axe. It is used as a unit of weight now.

新 实用汉语课本 入门级 汉字册

(14) 毛　　　ノ ニ 三 毛
máo　　　fur; *mao* (a measure word of Chinese
monetary unit, it is equal to 1/10 yuan)　4 strokes

(15) 戈　　　一 弋 戈 戈
gē　　　an ancient weapon　　　　4 strokes

3 认写课文中的汉字　Learn and write the Chinese characters in the text

(1) 光盘 guāngpán（光盤）

光 → 业 + 儿　　　　　6 strokes

盘 → 舟 + 皿　　　　　11 strokes

(2) 音乐 yīnyuè（音樂）

音 → 立 + 日　　　　　9 strokes

⺌ (chángzìtóur, the top of "常(cháng, constant)")
　　丶 丬 业 业 业　　　5 strokes

(3) 常常 chángcháng

常 → ⺌ + 口 + 巾　　　11 strokes

⻊ (zúzìpángr, the side of "足(zú, foot)", on the left side of a character, the seventh stroke in "足" is written as an upward stroke.)　丶 口 口 무 무 무 무　7 strokes

(4) 跟 gēn

跟 → ⻊ + 艮　　　　13 strokes

⼟ (títǔpángr, on the left side of a character, the third stroke of "土" is written as an upward stroke. It is called the side of "土".)　一 十 土　3 strokes

(5) 商场 shāngchǎng（商場）

商 → 亠 + ⧄ + 冂 + 八 + 口　11 strokes

场 → ⼟ + 易　　　　6 strokes

66

阝 (dān'ěrdāor, the side of "single-ear") ﻝ 阝 | 2 strokes

(6) 报纸 bàozhǐ（報紙）

报 → 扌 + 阝 + 又 | 7 strokes

(7) 梁祝 Liáng Zhù

梁 → 氵 + 刃 + 木 | 11 strokes

生 (gàozìtóur, the top of "告(gào, to tell)") 丿 ㇒ ㇏ 生 | 4 strokes

(8) 先生 xiānsheng

先 → 生 + 儿 | 6 strokes

(9) 要 yào

要 → 西 + 女 | 9 strokes

(10) 师傅 shīfu（師傅）

傅 (fù) → 亻 + 甫 + 寸 | 12 strokes

(The meaning side is "亻", and the phonetic side is "甫".)

(11) 香蕉 xiāngjiāo

香 → 禾 + 日 | 9 strokes

蕉 → 艹 + 隹 + 灬 | 15 strokes

(12) 苹果 píngguǒ（蘋果）

苹 → 艹 + 平 | 8 strokes

(The meaning is indicated by "艹" and the pronunciation is indicated by "平(píng)".)

(13) 对不起 duìbuqǐ（對不起）

对 → 又 + 寸 | 5 strokes

起 → 走 + 己 | 10 strokes

(14) 容易 róngyì

容 → 宀 ＋ 人 ＋ 口   10 strokes

易 → 日 ＋ 勿   8 strokes

钅 (jīnzìpángr, the side of "金(jīn, metal)") ノ ㇇ ㇇ ㇇ 钅 5 strokes

(On the left side of a character, "金" is written as "钅".)

(15) 钱 qián（錢）

钱 → 钅 ＋ 一 ＋ 戈   10 strokes

(16) 块 kuài（塊）

块 → 土 ＋ 夬   7 strokes

(17) 分 fēn

分 → 八 ＋ 刀   4 strokes

(Cut things in half with a knife.)

(18) 送 sòng

送 → 丷 ＋ 天 ＋ 辶   9 strokes

(19) 给 gěi（給）

给 → 纟 ＋ 合   9 strokes

(20) 找 zhǎo

找 → 扌 ＋ 戈   7 strokes

二 书写练习 Writing Exercises

1 按正确的笔顺描汉字，并在后边的空格里写汉字。

Trace over the characters, following the correct stroke order. Then copy the characters in the blank spaces.

舟	ノ 丿 月 月 舟 舟	舟	舟						

皿	丶冂四皿皿	皿	皿					
乐	一匚乐乐乐	乐	乐					
足	丶口口甲乷足足	足	足					
书	⁊乛书书	书	书					
本	一十才木本	本	本					
平	一丷二平平	平	平					
走	一十土丰丰走走	走	走					
己	⁊乛己	己	己					
穴	丶丷宀宂穴	穴	穴					
勿	丿勹勺勿	勿	勿					
金	丿人人今全全金金	金	金					
斤	丿丆斤斤	斤	斤					
毛	丿二三毛	毛	毛					
戈	一弋戈戈	戈	戈					

2 在空格里写汉字，注意汉字的部件。

Write the characters in the blank spaces, paying attention to the character components.

guāng	⺌＋儿	光						
pán	舟＋皿	盘						
yīn	立＋日	音						

cháng	⺌ + 口 + 巾	常						
gēn	⻊ + 艮	跟						
shāng	亠 + ⺍ + 冂 + 八 + 口	商						
chǎng	土 + 昜	场						
bào	扌 + 卩 + 又	报						
liáng	氵 + 刃 + 木	梁						
xiān	生 + 儿	先						
yào	西 + 女	要						
fù	亻 + 甫 + 寸	傅						
xiāng	禾 + 日	香						
jiāo	艹 + 隹 + 灬	蕉						
píng	艹 + 平	苹						
duì	又 + 寸	对						
qǐ	走 + 己	起						
róng	宀 + 八 + 口	容						
yì	日 + 勿	易						
qián	钅 + 一 + 戈	钱						
kuài	土 + 夬	块						
fēn	八 + 刀	分						

sòng	Ⱏ + 天 + 辶	送							
gěi	纟 + 人 + 一 + 口	给							
zhǎo	扌 + 戈	找							

3 把下列汉字分解成部件。

Divide the following characters into character components.

（1）是 → _____   （6）思 → _____

（2）星 → _____   （7）意 → _____

（3）兴 → _____   （8）贵 → _____

（4）爸 → _____   （9）高 → _____

（5）家 → _____   （10）京 → _____

4 为每个汉字标注拼音，并找到与它相应的图，然后连线。

Give the *pinyin* of the following characters and find the corresponding drawings. Draw a line to connect the two.

（1）羊

（2）日

（3）木

（4）水

（5）山

（6）月

（7）竹

（8）犬

（9）马

5 根据所给拼音，在第二行汉字中找到能与第一行汉字组成词语的汉字，然后连线。

Find a character in the second line which can be combined with a character in the first line to make a word according to the *pinyin* provided. Draw a line to connect the two.

（1）pútao　　（2）xiāngjiāo　　（3）píngguǒ　　（4）xiānsheng　　（5）xiǎojie

香　　　苹　　　葡　　　小　　　先

生　　　蕉　　　果　　　萄　　　姐

6 在空格里填上一个部件，使它和其他部件组成三个学过的汉字。

Fill in the blank with a character component to form three characters which we have learned.

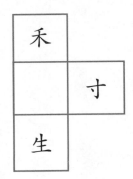

（Key to Exercise 6 in Lesson 9：汉、对）

72

7 用学过的汉字描述一次购物的经历。（不少于50个字）

Use the characters you have learned to describe a shopping experience (more than 50 characters).

_____

_____

_____

_____

我会说一点儿汉语

一 汉字学习 **Learning Chinese Characters**

1 汉字的结构(4) Structure of Chinese characters (4)

The enclosure structure ①

a. Four-sided enclosure

回 国 回

d. Top-left-bottom enclosure

回 医

b. Left-top-right enclosure

回 用 问

e. Top-right enclosure

回 可 司

c. Top-left enclosure

回 应 属

2 认写基本汉字 Learn and write basic Chinese characters

(1) 占   丨 卜 卜 占 占
zhàn   to occupy   5 strokes

(2) 里(裏)   丨 口 曰 日 甲 甲 里
lǐ   inside   7 strokes

(3) 至   一 乙 五 至 至 至
zhì   to   6 strokes

74

(4) 央　　ヽ 冂 叿 央 央
yāng　　center　　　　　　　　　5 strokes

(5) 东（東）　一 左 乐 夯 东
dōng　　east　　　　　　　　　5 strokes

(6) 西　　一 丆 冋 丙 西 西
xī　　west　　　　　　　　　6 strokes

(7) 免　　ノ ク 冎 色 色 争 免
miǎn　　to be excused from　　7 strokes

(8) 半　　ヽ ゛ 丷 兰 半
bàn　　half　　　　　　　　　5 strokes

(9) 与（與）　一 与 与
yǔ　　and　　　　　　　　　3 strokes

Note: Please differentiate "与" from "马".

(10) 页（頁）　一 丆 厂 页 页 页
yè　　page　　　　　　　　　6 strokes

(11) 以　　ㄥ ㄥ 以 以
yǐ　　to use　　　　　　　　4 strokes

3 认写课文中的汉字　Learn and write the Chinese characters in the text

(1) 司机 sījī（司機）

司 → 丁 + 一 + 口　　　　　　5 strokes

机 → 木 + 几　　　　　　　　6 strokes

(2) 点钟 diǎnzhōng（點鐘）

点 → 占 + 灬   9 strokes

钟 → 钅 + 中   9 strokes

丷 (yángzìpángr, the side of "羊(yáng, sheep)")

、丷丷䒑兰羊   6 strokes

(On the top or left side of a character, the vertical stroke in "羊" is written as a left-falling stroke "丿".)

(3) 差 chà

差 → 丷 + 工   9 strokes

刂 (lìdāopángr, on the right side of a multi-component character, "刀" is written as "刂". It is called the side of "standing knife".) 丨刂   2 strokes

亥 hài 、一亠亥亥亥   6 strokes

(4) 刻 kè

刻 → 亥 + 刂   8 strokes

(5) 回 huí

回 → 囗 + 口   6 strokes

(6) 能 néng

能 → 厶 + 月 + 匕 + 匕   10 strokes

(7) 到 dào

到 → 至 + 刂   8 strokes

(8) 英语 Yīngyǔ（英語）

英 → 艹 + 央   8 strokes

(9) 孙女儿 sūnnür（孫女兒）

孙 → 子 + 小   6 strokes

（10）岁数 suìshu（歲數）

数 —→ 米 ＋ 女 ＋ 攵   13 strokes

手（piěshǒu, the side of "slanting-hand"） ⺮ 二 三 手   4 strokes

（On the left side of a character, the fourth stroke in "手" is written as "丿".）

（11）拜拜 báibái

拜（bài）—→ 手 ＋ 一 ＋ 丰   9 strokes

（12）昨天 zuótiān

昨 —→ 日 ＋ 乍   9 strokes

（The side of "日" shows the character has a temporal connotation.）

（13）玩儿 wánr（玩兒）

玩 —→ 王 ＋ 元   8 strokes

（14）晚上 wǎnshang

晚 —→ 日 ＋ 免   11 strokes

（15）写 xiě（寫）

写 —→ ⼍ ＋ 与   5 strokes

垂 chuí ⼃ 二 三 乒 丢 丢 垂 垂   8 strokes

（16）睡觉 shuìjiào（睡覺）

睡 —→ 目 ＋ 垂   13 strokes

（Please note the left side of the character is the side of "目", not the side of "日". "Sleeping" is related to the "eyes".）

觉 —→ ⺍ ＋ 见   9 strokes

（17）起床 qǐchuáng

床 —→ 广 ＋ 木   7 strokes

(18) 应该 yīnggāi（應該）

应 → 广 + 业   7 strokes

该 → 讠 + 亥   8 strokes

(19) 问题 wèntí（問題）

题 → 是 + 页   15 strokes

(20) 陈 chén（陳）

陈 → 阝 + 东   7 strokes

二　书写练习　Writing Exercises

1 按正确的笔顺描汉字，并在后边的空格里写汉字。

Trace over the characters, following the correct stroke order. Then copy the characters in the blank spaces.

占	丨 卜 占 占 占	占	占					
里	丨 冂 日 日 甲 甲 里	里	里					
至	一 工 互 歪 至 至	至	至					
央	丨 冂 凹 央 央	央	央					
东	一 七 车 东 东	东	东					
西	一 丆 丙 丙 西 西	西	西					
免	丿 ⺈ ⺈ 冉 冉 免 免	免	免					
半	丶 丷 兰 半	半	半					

与	一 与 与	与	与					
页	一 丁 丆 页 页 页	页	页					
以	丨 ㇄ 以 以	以	以					

2 在空格里写汉字，注意汉字的部件。

Write the characters in the blank spaces, paying attention to the character components.

sī	刁 + 一 + 口	司						
jī	木 + 几	机						
diǎn	占 + 灬	点						
zhōng	钅 + 中	钟						
chà	𦍌 + 工	差						
kè	亥 + 刂	刻						
huí	囗 + 口	回						
néng	厶 + 月 + 匕 + 匕	能						
dào	至 + 刂	到						
yīng	艹 + 央	英						
sūn	子 + 小	孙						
shù	米 + 女 + 攵	数						
bài	手 + 一 + 丰	拜						

zuó	日 + 乍	昨						
wán	王 + 元	玩						
wǎn	日 + 免	晚						
xiě	冖 + 与	写						
shuì	目 + 千 + 艹 + 二	睡						
jiào	兴 + 见	觉						
chuáng	广 + 木	床						
yīng	广 + 业	应						
gāi	讠 + 亥	该						
tí	是 + 页	题						
chén	阝 + 东	陈						

3 把下列汉字分解成部件。

Divide the following characters into character components.

（1）国 → _____

（2）回 → _____

（3）问 → _____

（4）用 → _____

（5）属 → _____

（6）医 → _____

（7）可 → _____

（8）司 → _____

4 根据拼音写汉字。

Write characters according to the *pinyin*.

（1）天：zuótiān_____ jīntiān_____ míngtiān_____

（2）年：qùnián_____ jīnnián_____ míngnián_____

（3）午：shàngwǔ_____ zhōngwǔ_____ xiàwǔ_____

（4）学：xiǎoxué_____ zhōngxué_____ dàxué_____

5 为每个汉字标注拼音，并找到与它相应的图，然后连线。

Give the *pinyin* of the following characters and find the corresponding drawings. Draw a line to connect the two.

（1）下

（2）上

（3）门

（4）弓

（5）犬

（6）虫

（7）刀

（8）云

（9）井

（10）心

6 用汉字列出你的课程表。

Write a timetable of your classes in characters.

7 猜字谜。

Character riddle.

一字有两口，大口吃小口。

（ The key is a character. ）

（ Key to Exercise 6 in Lesson 10: 日 ）

8 用学过的汉字描述一次有趣的经历。（不少于50个字）

Use the characters you have learned to describe an interesting experience you have learned (more than 50 characters).

_____

_____

_____

_____

我全身都不舒服

一　汉字学习　Learning Chinese Characters

1　汉字的结构(5)　Structure of Chinese characters (5)

The enclosure structure ②

a. Left-bottom-right enclosure

画

b. Left-bottom enclosure

这　起　题

2　认写基本汉字　Learn and write basic Chinese characters

(1) 予　ㄱ ㄲ マ 予
yǔ　to give　4 strokes

(2) 母　ㄥ 口 口 口 母
mǔ　mother　5 strokes

(3) 冬　ノ ク 夂 冬 冬
dōng　winter　5 strokes

(4) 令　ノ 人 ム 今 令
lìng　order　5 strokes

(5) 牙　一 二 于 牙
yá　tooth　4 strokes

(6) 衣 　　` 一 ナ ナ 衣 衣
yī　　　clothes　　　　　　　　　　6 strokes

(7) 自 　　' 亻 白 白 自 自
zì　　　self　　　　　　　　　　6 strokes

(8) 发（發）　一 ナ 发 发 发
fā　　　to send out　　　　　　5 strokes

(9) 主 　　` 一 亠 丰 主
zhǔ　　host　　　　　　　　　　5 strokes

(10) 厂（廠）　一 厂
chǎng　factory　　　　　　　　2 strokes

3 认写课文中的汉字　Learn and write the Chinese characters in the text

(1) 全身 quánshēn

全 → 人 ＋ 王　　　　　　　6 strokes

(2) 舒服 shūfu

舒 → 人 ＋ 舌 ＋ 予　　　12 strokes

服（fú）→ 月 ＋ 卩 ＋ 又　　8 strokes

亻 (wòrénpángr, the side of "sleeping person")　丿 亻　2 strokes

(3) 每 měi

每 → 𠂉 ＋ 母　　　　　　7 strokes

火 (huǒzìpángr, on the left side of a multi-component character, the fourth stroke in "火" is written as a dot. It is called the side of "火".)

　` 丷 灯 灯　　　　　　4 strokes

(4) 锻炼 duànliàn（鍛煉）

锻 → 钅 + 段　　　　　　　　　14 strokes

(The meaning side is "钅" and the phonetic side is "段 (duàn)".)

炼 → 火 + 东　　　　　　　　　9 strokes

疒 (bìngzìpángr, the side of "病(bìng, illness)" denotes disease or ailment.)

丶 亠 广 疒 疒　　　　　　　　　5 strokes

(5) 疼 téng

疼 → 疒 + 冬　　　　　　　　　10 strokes

(The "illness" side denotes the meaning and "冬 (dōng)" indicates the pronunciation.)

(6) 嗓子 sǎngzi

嗓 → 口 + 又 + 又 + 又 + 木　　13 strokes

(7) 想 xiǎng

想 → 木 + 目 + 心　　　　　　　13 strokes

(The meaning part is "心" and the phonetic part is "相(xiāng)".)

(8) 看病 kànbìng

病 → 疒 + 丙　　　　　　　　　10 strokes

(The meaning side is "疒" and the phonetic side is "丙(bǐng)".)

(9) 身体 shēntǐ（身體）

体 → 亻 + 本　　　　　　　　　7 strokes

(10) 吧 ba

吧 → 口 + 巴　　　　　　　　　7 strokes

(The meaning side is "口" and the phonetic side is "巴".)

冫 (liǎngdiǎnshuǐr, the side of "two-drops-of-water") 丶 冫　　2 strokes

(11) 冷 lěng

冷 → 冫 + 令　　　　　　　　　　7 strokes

(12) 穿 chuān

穿 → 穴 + 牙　　　　　　　　　　9 strokes

(13) 休息 xiūxi

休 → 亻 + 木　　　　　　　　　　6 strokes

息 (xī) → 自 + 心　　　　　　　　10 strokes

(14) 挂号 guàhào（掛號）

挂 → 扌 + 土 + 土　　　　　　　9 strokes

(15) 发炎 fāyán（發炎）

炎 → 火 + 火　　　　　　　　　　8 strokes

戈 (yáozìtóur, the top of "尧(yáo, eminent)") 一 弋 戈　　3 strokes
(Please differentiate it from "戈(gē)".)

(16) 发烧 fāshāo（發燒）

烧 → 火 + 戈 + 兀　　　　　　　10 strokes

(17) 感冒 gǎnmào

感 → 戌 + 一 + 口 + 心　　　　　13 strokes

冒 → 曰 + 目　　　　　　　　　　9 strokes

(18) 住院 zhùyuàn

住 → 亻 + 主　　　　　　　　　　7 strokes
(The meaning side is "亻" and the phonetic side is "主(zhǔ)".)

（19）中药 zhōngyào（中藥）

药 → 艹 ＋ 纟 ＋ 勺   9 strokes

（20）愿意 yuànyì（願意）

愿 → 厂 ＋ 白 ＋ 小 ＋ 心   14 strokes

二　书写练习　Writing Exercises

1 按正确的笔顺描汉字，并在后边的空格里写汉字。

Trace over the characters, following the correct stroke order. Then copy the characters in the blank spaces.

予	フ マ 五 予	予	予					
母	㇄ 孖 孖 母 母	母	母					
冬	ノ ク 久 冬 冬	冬	冬					
令	ノ 人 人 今 令	令	令					
牙	一 二 于 牙	牙	牙					
衣	、 一 ナ 齐 衣 衣	衣	衣					
自	′ 亻 白 白 自 自	自	自					
发	一 ナ 步 发 发	发	发					
主	、 一 三 主 主	主	主					
厂	一 厂	厂	厂					

实用汉语课本 入门级 汉字册

2 在空格里写汉字，注意汉字的部件。

Write the characters in the blank spaces, paying attention to the character components.

quán	人 + 王	全							
shū	人 + 干 + 口 + 予	舒							
fú	月 + 卩 + 又	服							
měi	𠂉 + 母	每							
duàn	钅 + 段	锻							
liàn	火 + 东	炼							
téng	疒 + 冬	疼							
sǎng	口 + 又 + 又 + 又 + 木	嗓							
xiǎng	木 + 目 + 心	想							
bìng	疒 + 丙	病							
tǐ	亻 + 本	体							
ba	口 + 巴	吧							
lěng	冫 + 令	冷							
chuān	穴 + 牙	穿							
xiū	亻 + 木	休							
xī	自 + 心	息							
guà	扌 + 土 + 土	挂							

88

pinyin	components	字						
yán	火 + 火	炎						
shāo	火 + 戈 + 兀	烧						
gǎn	戌 + 一 + 口 + 心	感						
mào	冃 + 目	冒						
zhù	亻 + 主	住						
yào	艹 + 纟 + 勺	药						
yuàn	厂 + 白 + 小 + 心	愿						

3 把下列汉字分解成部件。

Divide the following characters into character components.

（1）出 → _____　　（4）起 → _____

（2）画 → _____　　（5）题 → _____

（3）进 → _____

4 为下列汉字标注拼音，并在括号里写出笔画数。

Give the *pinyin* of the following characters and write the stroke numbers in the parentheses.

（1）广_____（　　）　　（4）几_____（　　）

　　厂_____（　　）　　　几_____（　　）

（2）今_____（　　）　　（5）问_____（　　）

　　令_____（　　）　　　间_____（　　）

（3）全_____（　　）　　（6）目_____（　　）

　　金_____（　　）　　　自_____（　　）

（7）太＿＿＿＿＿＿（　　）　　　　（9）主＿＿＿＿＿＿（　　）

　　　大＿＿＿＿＿＿（　　）　　　　　　王＿＿＿＿＿＿（　　）

（8）休＿＿＿＿＿＿（　　）　　　（10）作＿＿＿＿＿＿（　　）

　　　体＿＿＿＿＿＿（　　）　　　　　　昨＿＿＿＿＿＿（　　）

5 根据所给拼音，在第二行汉字中找到能与第一行汉字组成词语的汉字，然后连线。

Find a character in the second line which can be combined with a character in the first line to make a word according to the *pinyin* provided. Draw a line to connect the two.

（1）yīnggāi　　（2）shuìjiào　　（3）shūfu　　（4）duànliàn　　（5）shēntǐ

　　身　　　　　应　　　　　睡　　　　　舒　　　　　锻

　　服　　　　　觉　　　　　体　　　　　炼　　　　　该

6 用汉字填写学生卡。

Fill in the studuent card with characters.

学生卡

姓名		性别	国籍	
出生年月日			出生地	

New words：

① 卡　　　　kǎ　　　　　　N　　　　card

② 姓名　　　xìngmíng　　N　　　　name

③ 性别　　　xìngbié　　　N　　　　sex

④ 国籍　　　guójí　　　　N　　　　nationality

7 猜字谜。

Character riddle.

山外有山。

（ The key is a character. ）

（ Key to Exercise 7 in Lesson 11: 回 ）

8 用学过的汉字描述你们国家的一个节日。（不少于50个字）

Use the characters you have learned to describe a festival in your country (more than 50 characters).

_____

_____

_____

_____

9 用学过的汉字描述一次看病的经历。（不少于50个字）

Use the characters you have learned to describe your experience of seeing a doctor (more than 50 characters).

_____

_____

_____

_____

第十三课
Lesson 13

我认识了一个漂亮的姑娘

一　汉字学习　Learning Chinese Characters

1 部首查字法　Consulting a Chinese dictionary based on radicals

Many Chinese character dictionaries are compiled according to the order of the characters' "radicals". Radicals are common components, located on the top, bottom, left, right, or outer part of characters, which usually indicate the category of meaning to which a character belongs. For example, "好", "她", "妈", "姐", "妹", "姓", and "娜" are grouped under the radical "女", which is the common component on the left side of these characters. However, "意", "思", "想", "您", and "愿" are grouped under the radical "心", which is the common component at the bottom of these characters.

In the radical index of a dictionary, radicals are listed in order according to the number of their strokes. In the index of entries, characters of the same radical are arranged in groups according to the number of their strokes excluding those of the radical.

Therefore, after determining the radical of a character, you should count the number of strokes in the radical and consult the radical index to obtain the page number where the radical entry can be found in the index of entries. Then, count the number of strokes in the character excluding the radical and consult the corresponding group to find the character and its page number in the dictionary. For example, the character "锻" will be found under the "钅" radical and in the section containing characters with 9 strokes apart from those of the radical.

2 认写基本汉字　Learn and write basic Chinese characters

(1) 古　　　一 十 古 古 古
gǔ　　ancient　　　　　　5 strokes

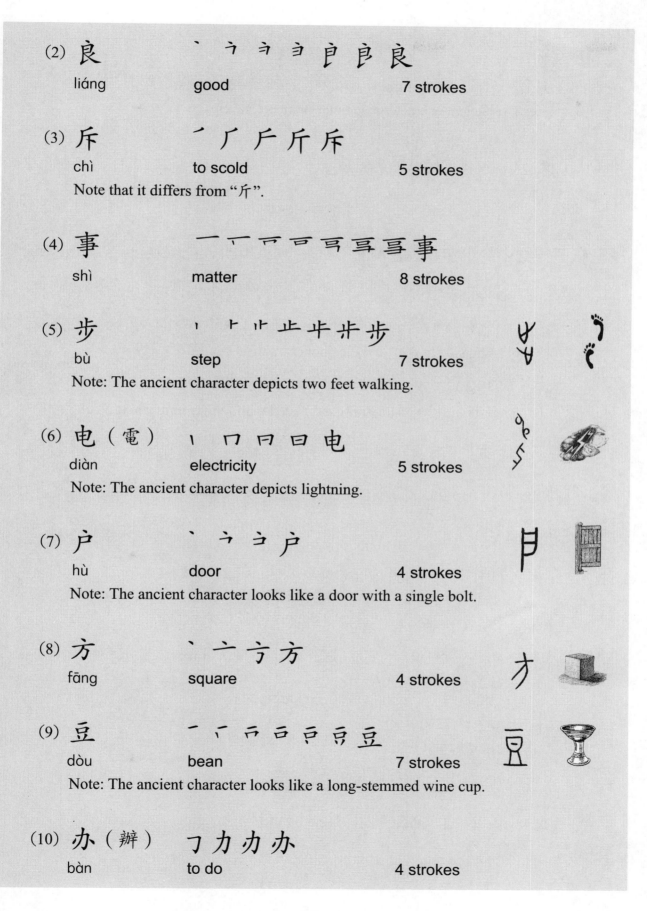

(2) 良　丶 ㇇ ⺕ ⺕ 艮 艮 良
liáng　good　7 strokes

(3) 斥　㇒ 厂 斤 斤 斥
chì　to scold　5 strokes
Note that it differs from “斤”.

(4) 事　一 ㇀ 冖 ⼝ 亖 亖 亖 事
shì　matter　8 strokes

(5) 步　丨 ⺊ 止 止 步 步 步
bù　step　7 strokes
Note: The ancient character depicts two feet walking.

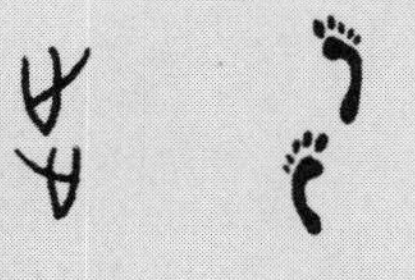

(6) 电（電）　丨 冂 冂 日 电
diàn　electricity　5 strokes
Note: The ancient character depicts lightning.

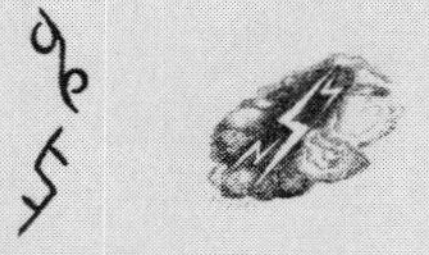

(7) 户　丶 ㇇ ⺕ 户
hù　door　4 strokes
Note: The ancient character looks like a door with a single bolt.

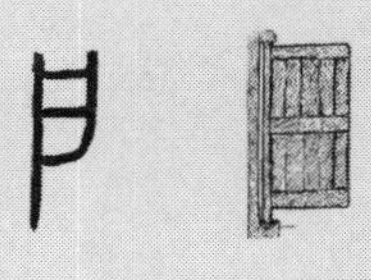

(8) 方　丶 亠 亢 方
fāng　square　4 strokes

(9) 豆　一 ㇀ 冖 口 ⼝ 豆 豆
dòu　bean　7 strokes
Note: The ancient character looks like a long-stemmed wine cup.

(10) 办（辦）　㇇ 力 办 办
bàn　to do　4 strokes

(11) 竹 　　ノ 𠂉 𠂉 竹 竹 竹

zhú　　　　bamboo　　　　　　　　　6 strokes

Note: The ancient character resembles bamboo leaves.

(12) 反 　　一 厂 厉 反

fǎn　　　　reverse　　　　　　　　　4 strokes

3 认写课文中的汉字　Learn and write the Chinese characters in the text

(1) 姑娘 gūniang

姑 → 女 + 古　　　　　　　　　8 strokes

(The meaning side is "女" and the phonetic side is "古(gǔ)".)

娘 (niáng) → 女 + 良　　　　　10 strokes

("女" suggests that the character is associated with female in meaning.)

(2) 听说 tīngshuō (聽說)

听 → 口 + 斤　　　　　　　　　7 strokes

(3) 得 dé

得 → 彳 + 日 + 一 + 寸　　　　11 strokes

(4) 告诉 gàosu (告訴)

告 → 牛 + 口　　　　　　　　　7 strokes

(The meaning side is "口".)

诉 (sù) → 讠 + 斤　　　　　　　7 strokes

(The meaning side is "讠".)

(5) 件 jiàn

件 → 亻 + 牛　　　　　　　　　6 strokes

(6) 散步 sànbù

散 → 龷 ＋ 月 ＋ 攵   12 strokes

(7) 电影 diànyǐng（電影）

影 → 日 ＋ 京 ＋ 彡   15 strokes

(8) 咖啡 kāfēi

咖 → 口 ＋ 力 ＋ 口   8 strokes

啡 → 口 ＋ 非   11 strokes

(The meaning side is "口" and the phonetic side is "非(fēi)".)

(9) 宿舍 sùshè

宿 → 宀 ＋ 亻 ＋ 百   11 strokes

("宀" denotes a house, "百" shows a mat, and "亻" suggests a person.)

舍 → 人 ＋ 舌   8 strokes

("人" denotes a shelter and "舌(shé)" indicates the pronunciation.)

(10) 房子 fángzi

房 → 户 ＋ 方   8 strokes

(The meaning is suggested by "户(hù)" and the pronunciation is shown by "方(fāng)".)

(11) 租 zū

租 → 禾 ＋ 且   10 strokes

(12) 厨房 chúfáng

厨 → 厂 ＋ 豆 ＋ 寸   12 strokes

(13) 厕所 cèsuǒ（廁所）

厕 → 厂 + 贝 + 刂　　　　　8 strokes

所 → 戶 + 斤　　　　　　　8 strokes

(14) 公司 gōngsī

公 → 八 + 厶　　　　　　　4 strokes

(15) 打 dǎ

打 → 扌 + 丁　　　　　　　5 strokes

(16) 电话 diànhuà（電話）

话 → 讠 + 舌　　　　　　　8 strokes

(Speaking is related to the tongue, "舌(shé)".)

(17) 让 ràng（讓）

让 → 讠 + 上　　　　　　　5 strokes

(18) 帮助 bāngzhù（幫助）

帮 → 邦 + 巾　　　　　　　9 strokes

("邦(bāng)" denotes the pronunciation.)

助 → 且 + 力　　　　　　　7 strokes

(19) 喂 wèi

喂 → 口 + 田 + 𧘇（𧘇：一丆丂𧘇）　12 strokes

(20) 位 wèi

位 → 亻 + 立　　　　　　　7 strokes

圣 (qīngzìbiānr, the side of "轻(qīng, light)")

フ フ 三 至 圣　　　　　　　5 strokes

(21) 经理 jīnglǐ（經理）

经 → 纟 + 圣　　　　　8 strokes

理 → 王 + 里　　　　　11 strokes

("里" indicates the pronunciation.)

饣 (shízìpángr, the side of "食(shí, food)")　ノ 亇 饣　3 strokes

(22) 吃饭 chīfàn（吃飯）

饭 → 饣 + 反　　　　　7 strokes

竹 (zhúzìtóur, the top of "竹(zhú, bamboo)", the vertical stroke and the vertical stroke with a hook in "竹" are both written as a dot, when this character is on the top of a multi-component character.)　ノ 亇 亇 钋 竹 竹　6 strokes

(23) 等 děng

等 → 竹 + 土 + 寸　　　12 strokes

二　书写练习　Writing Exercises

1 按正确的笔顺描汉字，并在后边的空格里写汉字。

Trace over the characters, following the correct stroke order. Then copy the characters in the blank spaces.

古	一 十 十 古 古	古	古				
良	丶 ㇇ ㇕ ㅋ 皀 良 良	良	良				
斤	丿 厂 斤 斤	斤	斤				
事	一 ㅜ ㅜ 百 写 写 事	事	事				

步	㇐㇒止少步	步	步						
电	丨冂曰日电	电	电						
户	丶㇐㇒户	户	户						
方	丶一方方	方	方						
豆	一㇑曰豆豆豆	豆	豆						
办	㇋力力办	办	办						
竹	㇒㇒㇒竹竹竹	竹	竹						
反	一厂反反	反	反						

2 在空格里写汉字，注意汉字的部件。

Write the characters in the blank spaces, paying attention to the character components.

gū	女 + 古	姑							
niáng	女 + 良	娘							
tīng	口 + 斤	听							
dé	彳 + 日 + 一 + 寸	得							
gào	生 + 口	告							
sù	讠 + 斥	诉							
jiàn	亻 + 牛	件							
sàn	艹 + 月 + 攵	散							

yǐng	日 + 京 + 彡	影							
kā	口 + 力 + 口	咖							
fēi	口 + 非	啡							
sù	宀 + 亻 + 百	宿							
shè	人 + 舌	舍							
fáng	户 + 方	房							
zū	禾 + 且	租							
chú	厂 + 豆 + 寸	厨							
cè	厂 + 贝 + 刂	厕							
suǒ	户 + 斤	所							
gōng	八 + 厶	公							
dǎ	扌 + 丁	打							
huà	讠 + 舌	话							
ràng	讠 + 上	让							
bāng	丰 + 阝 + 巾	帮							
zhù	且 + 力	助							
wèi	口 + 田 + 氏	喂							
wèi	亻 + 立	位							

jīng	纟 + 巠	经						
lǐ	王 + 里	理						
fàn	饣 + 反	饭						
děng	竹 + 土 + 寸	等						

3 为下列汉字标注拼音，并把每一组汉字相同的部首写在括号里。

Give the *pinyin* of the following characters and write the radical common to the characters in each group in the parenthesis.

（1）妈＿＿＿ 姐＿＿＿ 妹＿＿＿ 好＿＿＿ 姑＿＿＿ 娘＿＿＿

　　她＿＿＿ 娜＿＿＿ 　　　　　　　　　　　　　　（　　　）

（2）他＿＿＿ 你＿＿＿ 们＿＿＿ 做＿＿＿ 件＿＿＿ 什＿＿＿

　　休＿＿＿ 体＿＿＿ 作＿＿＿ 化＿＿＿ 住＿＿＿ 位＿＿＿

　　候＿＿＿ 　　　　　　　　　　　　　　　　　　　（　　　）

（3）语＿＿＿ 请＿＿＿ 谁＿＿＿ 谢＿＿＿ 让＿＿＿ 认＿＿＿

　　识＿＿＿ 说＿＿＿ 话＿＿＿ 诉＿＿＿ 课＿＿＿ 该＿＿＿（　　　）

（4）吗＿＿＿ 吧＿＿＿ 叫＿＿＿ 吃＿＿＿ 喝＿＿＿ 号＿＿＿

　　只＿＿＿ 哪＿＿＿ 告＿＿＿ 呢＿＿＿ 嗓＿＿＿ 喂＿＿＿

　　啊＿＿＿ 咖＿＿＿ 啡＿＿＿ 可＿＿＿ 听　　　　　（　　　）

（5）这＿＿＿ 进＿＿＿ 还＿＿＿ 送＿＿＿ 　　　　　　　（　　　）

4 朗读并写汉字。

Read and copy the following characters indicating numbers.

读音 Pronunciation	yī	èr	sān	sì	wǔ	liù	qī	bā	jiǔ	shí
小写 Ordinary form	一	二	三	四	五	六	七	八	九	十
大写 Capital form	壹	贰	叁	肆	伍	陆	柒	捌	玖	拾
描写 Trace	壹	贰	叁	肆	伍	陆	柒	捌	玖	拾
临写 Copy										

5 猜字谜。

Character riddle.

太少了一点儿。

（ The key is a character. ）

（ Key to Exercise 7 in Lesson 12: 出 ）

6 用学过的汉字描述你的宿舍或你的家。（不少于50个字）

Use the characters you have learned to describe your dormitory or your home (more than 50 characters).

_____

_____

_____

_____

第十四课
Lesson 14

复习
Review

祝你圣诞快乐

一 汉字学习 Learning Chinese Characters

1 音序查字法 Consulting a Chinese dictionary based on *pinyin*

In many Chinese dictionaries, the entries are arranged alphabetically according to Chinese phonetics (*Hanyu pinyin*). Characters with the same *pinyin* spelling are put under the same entry and then sub-divided according to their tones. Characters in the same tone group are arranged in order, according to their number of strokes. When the pronunciation of a character is known, it is easy to find a character in this type of dictionary.

2 认写基本汉字 Learn and write basic Chinese characters

(1) 才　　一 十 才
cái　　just　　　　　　3 strokes

(2) 由　　丨 冂 日 由 由
yóu　　by　　　　　　5 strokes

(3) 州　　丶 丿 少 州 州 州
zhōu　　state　　　　6 strokes

Note: "川 (chuān)" is the drawing of a river and the three dots "丶" show its islets.

3 认写课文中的汉字 Learn and write the Chinese characters in the text

廴 (jiànzhīpángr, the side of "建(jiàn, to construct)") ㇋ 廴 2 strokes

(1) 圣诞 Shèngdàn（聖誕）

圣 → 又 + 土 5 strokes

诞 → 讠 + 正 + 廴 8 strokes

(2) 刚才 gāngcái（剛才）

刚 → 冈 + 刂 6 strokes

(The pronunciation is indicated by "冈(gāng)".)

(3) 邮局 yóujú（郵局）

邮 → 由 + 阝 7 strokes

(The pronunciation is shown by "由(yóu)".)

局 → 尸 + 可 7 strokes

(4) 寄 jì

寄 → 宀 + 大 + 可 11 strokes

(5) 打扫 dǎsǎo（打掃）

扫 → 扌 + 彐 6 strokes

(The meaning is indicated by "扌".)

(6) 脏 zāng（髒）

脏 → 月 + 广 + 土 10 strokes

(7) 洗 xǐ

洗 → 氵 + 先 9 strokes

(8) 外婆 wàipó

婆 → 波 ＋ 女　　　　　　　　　11 strokes

(9) 南方 nánfāng

南 → 十 ＋ 冂 ＋ 羊　　　　　9 strokes

方 (lǚzìbiānr, the side of "旅(lǚ, travel)")　ㆍ ㇇ 方 方　4 strokes

丁 chù　ㄧ 二 丁　　　　　3 strokes

(10) 旅行 lǚxíng

旅 → 方 ＋ 乚 ＋ 民　　　　10 strokes

行 → 彳 ＋ 丁　　　　　　6 strokes

(11) 留学生 liúxuéshēng（留學生）

留 → 𠂉 ＋ 刀 ＋ 田（𠂉：ㆍ 𠂉 𠂉）　10 strokes

(12) 念 niàn

念 → 今 ＋ 心　　　　　　　8 strokes

(13) 生词 shēngcí（生詞）

词 → 讠 ＋ 司　　　　　　　7 strokes

(14) 复习 fùxí（複習）

复 → 𠂉 ＋ 日 ＋ 夂　　　　9 strokes

(15) 练习 liànxí（練習）

练 → 纟 ＋ 东　　　　　　　8 strokes

(16) 语法 yǔfǎ（語法）

法 → 氵 ＋ 去　　　　　　　8 strokes

(17) 节 jié（節）

节 → 艹 + 卩　　　　　　　　　　　5 strokes

牛　(niúzìpángr, the side of "牛(niú, ox)")

丿 ㇒ 牜 牜　　　　　　　　　　　4 strokes

(On the left side of a multi-component character, "牛" is written as "牜".)

(18) 礼物 lǐwù（禮物）

礼 → 礻 + 乚　　　　　　　　　　　5 strokes

物 → 牜 + 勿　　　　　　　　　　　8 strokes

(The pronunciation is indicated by "勿".)

(19) 欧洲 Ōuzhōu（歐洲）

欧 → 区 + 欠　　　　　　　　　　　8 strokes

洲 → 氵 + 州　　　　　　　　　　　9 strokes

(The meaning side is "氵" and the phonetic side is "州(zhōu)". The character "洲" means an islet in a river or a continent in an ocean.)

(20) 上海 Shànghǎi

海 → 氵 + 每　　　　　　　　　　　10 strokes

(The meaning side is "氵".)

二　书写练习　Writing Exercises

1 按正确的笔顺描汉字，并在后边的空格里写汉字。

Trace over the characters, following the correct stroke order. Then copy the characters in the blank spaces.

才	一 十 才		才	才							

| 由 | 丨冂曰由由 | 由 | 由 | | | | | | |
| 州 | 丶丿丬州州州 | 州 | 州 | | | | | | |

2 在空格里写汉字，注意汉字的部件。

Write the characters in the blank spaces, paying attention to the character components.

shèng	又 + 土	圣							
dàn	讠 + 正 + 又	诞							
gāng	冈 + 刂	刚							
yóu	由 + 阝	邮							
jú	尸 + 句	局							
jì	宀 + 大 + 可	寄							
sǎo	扌 + 彐	扫							
zāng	月 + 广 + 土	脏							
xǐ	氵 + 先	洗							
pó	氵 + 皮 + 女	婆							
nán	十 + 冂 + 羊	南							
lǚ	方 + 𠂉 + 氏	旅							
xíng	彳 + 亍	行							
liú	𠃌 + 刀 + 田	留							

niàn	今 + 心	念								
cí	讠 + 司	词								
fù	𠂉 + 日 + 夂	复								
liàn	纟 + 东	练								
fǎ	氵 + 去	法								
jié	艹 + 卩	节								
lǐ	礻 + 乚	礼								
wù	牜 + 勿	物								
ōu	区 + 欠	欧								
zhōu	氵 + 州	洲								
hǎi	氵 + 每	海								

3 为下列汉字标注拼音，并把每一组汉字相同的部首写在括号里。

Give the *pinyin* of the following characters and write the radical common to the characters in each group in the parenthesis.

（1）打＿＿　找＿＿　扫＿＿　挂＿＿　授＿＿　报＿＿　（　　）

（2）念＿＿　想＿＿　意＿＿　思＿＿　愿＿＿　感＿＿　（　　）

（3）绍＿＿　红＿＿　经＿＿　给＿＿　练＿＿　（　　）

（4）友＿＿　发＿＿　圣＿＿　对＿＿　欢＿＿　（　　）

（5）汉＿＿　酒＿＿　法＿＿　游＿＿　泳＿＿　没＿＿

　　海＿＿　洲＿＿　洗＿＿　漂＿＿　波＿＿　（　　）

（6）英＿＿　苹＿＿　药＿＿　蕉＿＿　葡＿＿　萄＿＿　（　　）

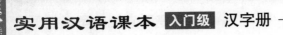

（7）会____ 舍____ 全____ 金____ 今____ 拿____ 　　（　　）

（8）时____ 明____ 昨____ 晚____ 星____ 是____ 　　（　　）

4 为下列每组汉字和词语标注拼音，并把它们译成英文。

Give the *pinyin* for the following groups of characters and words and then translate them into English.

（1）学_____ _____

　　学习_____ _____　　　　学院_____ _____

　　学生_____ _____　　　　大学_____ _____

（2）语_____ _____

　　汉语_____ _____　　　　英语_____ _____

　　外语_____ _____　　　　语法_____ _____

（3）国_____ _____

　　中国_____ _____　　　　英国_____ _____

　　美国_____ _____　　　　外国_____ _____

（4）方_____ _____

　　南方_____ _____　　　　东方_____ _____

　　北方_____ _____　　　　西方_____ _____

（Key to Exercise 5 in Lesson 13: 大）

5 用学过的汉字描述圣诞节的情景。（不少于50个字）

Use the characters you have learned to describe the situation of Christmas Day (more than 50 characters).

_____

_____

_____

_____

附录 **Appendices**

汉字索引
Chinese Character Index in the Textbook

A

啊	à	7
爱	ài	8

B

八	bā	1
巴	bā	7
爸	bà	7
吧	ba	12
白	bái	4
百	bǎi	8
拜	bài	11
办	bàn	13
半	bàn	11
帮	bāng	13
报	bào	10
北	běi	9
贝	bèi	3
本	běn	10
匕	bǐ	3
病	bìng	12
波	bō	7
卜	bǔ	8
不	bù	2
步	bù	13

C

才	cái	14
参	cān	9
厕	cè	13
差	chà	11
常	cháng	10
厂	chǎng	12
场	chǎng	10
陈	chén	11
吃	chī	9
斥	chì	13
虫	chóng	9
出	chū	9
厨	chú	13
穿	chuān	12
床	chuáng	11
词	cí	13
寸	cùn	6

D

打	dǎ	13
大	dà	2
诞	dàn	14
蛋	dàn	9
当	dāng	8

刀	dāo	2
到	dào	11
得	dé	13
的	de	4
等	děng	13
弟	dì	8
点	diǎn	11
电	diàn	13
丁	dīng	2
东	dōng	11
冬	dōng	12
都	dōu	3
豆	dòu	13
锻	duàn	12
对	duì	10
兑	duì	6
多	duō	8

E

儿	ér	5
耳	ěr	9
二	èr	5

F

发	fā	12

法	fǎ	14	贵	guì	4	间	jiān	6
反	fǎn	13	国	guó	3	见	jiàn	5
饭	fàn	13	果	guǒ	9	件	jiàn	13
方	fāng	13				蕉	jiāo	10
房	fáng	13	**H**			叫	jiào	4
啡	fēi	13				觉	jiào	11
分	fēn	10	还	hái	8	教	jiào	7
服	fú	12	海	hǎi	14	节	jié	14
父	fù	7	汉	hàn	4	姐	jiě	5
复	fù	14	好	hǎo	5	介	jiè	7
傅	fù	10	号	hào	9	斤	jīn	10
			喝	hē	9	今	jīn	9
G			禾	hé	8	金	jīn	10
			和	hé	8	进	jìn	5
该	gāi	11	贺	hè	9	京	jīng	9
感	gǎn	12	很	hěn	7	经	jīng	13
刚	gāng	14	红	hóng	9	井	jǐng	5
高	gāo	7	候	hòu	6	九	jiǔ	6
糕	gāo	9	户	hù	13	酒	jiǔ	9
告	gào	13	华	huá	9	局	jú	14
戈	gē	10	话	huà	13	聚	jù	9
哥	gē	2	欢	huān	8			
个	gè	8	回	huí	11	**K**		
给	gěi	10	会	huì	9			
跟	gēn	10	火	huǒ	1	咖	kā	13
工	gōng	6				开	kāi	7
弓	gōng	7	**J**			看	kàn	7
公	gōng	13				烤	kǎo	9
共	gòng	8	机	jī	11	可	kě	2
狗	gǒu	8	几	jǐ	8	刻	kè	11
姑	gū	13	己	jǐ	10	课	kè	9
古	gǔ	13	寄	jì	14	口	kǒu	2
挂	guà	12	加	jiā	7	块	kuài	10
光	guāng	10	家	jiā	8	快	kuài	9

R

然	rán	8
让	ràng	13
人	rén	3
认	rèn	4
日	rì	3
容	róng	10

S

三	sān	6
散	sǎn	13
嗓	sǎng	12
扫	sǎo	14
商	shāng	10
上	shàng	9
烧	shāo	12
少	shǎo	8
绍	shào	7
舍	shě	13
谁	shéi	7
身	shēn	6
什	shén	6
生	shēng	3
圣	shèng	14
尸	shī	9
师	shī	3
十	shí	3
时	shí	6
识	shí	4
矢	shǐ	3
士	shì	8
事	shì	13
是	shì	3
手	shǒu	4
寿	shòu	9
授	shòu	7
书	shū	10
舒	shū	12
属	shǔ	9
术	shù	7
数	shù	11
水	shuǐ	4
睡	shuì	11
说	shuō	6
厶	sī	6
司	sī	11
思	sī	6
四	sì	5
宋	sòng	9
送	sòng	10
诉	sù	13
宿	sù	13
岁	suì	9
孙	sūn	11
所	suǒ	13

T

他	tā	3
她	tā	3
太	tài	6
萄	táo	9
疼	téng	12
题	tí	11
体	tǐ	12
天	tiān	6
田	tián	4
听	tīng	13
头	tóu	9
土	tǔ	2

W

瓦	wǎ	9
外	wài	8
玩	wán	11
晚	wǎn	11
亡	wáng	6
为	wèi	7
未	wèi	8
位	wèi	13
喂	wèi	13
文	wén	5
问	wèn	5
我	wǒ	1
五	wǔ	9
午	wǔ	9
勿	wù	10
物	wù	14

X

夕	xī	8
西	xī	11
息	xī	12
习	xí	7
洗	xǐ	14
喜	xǐ	8
系	xì	7
下	xià	7

先	xiān	10	易	yì	10	者	zhě	3
现	xiàn	6	意	yì	6	这	zhè	5
香	xiāng	10	音	yīn	10	真	zhēn	8
想	xiǎng	12	应	yīng	11	只	zhǐ	4
小	xiǎo	4	英	yīng	11	至	zhì	11
写	xiě	11	影	yǐng	13	中	zhōng	3
谢	xiè	6	用	yòng	5	钟	zhōng	11
心	xīn	4	由	yóu	14	舟	zhōu	10
星	xīng	9	邮	yóu	14	州	zhōu	14
行	xíng	14	友	yǒu	4	洲	zhōu	14
兴	xìng	7	有	yǒu	6	竹	zhú	13
姓	xìng	4	又	yòu	2	主	zhǔ	12
休	xiū	12	与	yǔ	11	助	zhù	13
穴	xué	10	予	yǔ	12	住	zhù	12
学	xué	5	语	yǔ	4	祝	zhù	9
			玉	yù	3	专	zhuān	7
Y			元	yuán	7	子	zǐ	5
			院	yuàn	7	自	zì	12
鸭	yā	9	愿	yuàn	12	字	zì	7
牙	yá	12	月	yuè	4	走	zǒu	10
言	yán	4	乐	yuè	10	租	zū	13
炎	yán	12	云	yún	8	足	zú	10
央	yāng	11				昨	zuó	11
羊	yáng	7	**Z**			作	zuò	8
样	yàng	9				坐	zuò	5
药	yào	12	再	zài	5	做	zuò	8
要	yào	10	在	zài	5			
也	yě	1	脏	zāng	14			
业	yè	7	怎	zěn	9			
页	yè	11	占	zhàn	11			
一	yī	1	张	zhāng	7			
衣	yī	12	长	zhǎng	7			
医	yī	3	找	zhǎo	10			
以	yǐ	11	照	zhào	8			

部 首 Radieals	名 称 Names	例 字 Examples
厂	偏厂儿（piānchǎngr）	历、厕、厨
匚	区字框儿（qūzìkuàngr）	区、巨、医
刂	立刀旁儿（lìdāopángr）	利、到、刻
冂	同字框儿（tóngzìkuàngr）	冈、网、同
几	周字框儿（zhōuzìkuàngr）	用、甩、周
亻	单人旁儿（dānrénpángr）	他、休、住
勹	包字头儿（bāozìtóur）	句、包、狗
亠	京字头儿（jīngzìtóur）	市、京、夜
冫	两点水儿（liǎngdiǎnshuǐr）	冷、冰、冻
宀	秃宝盖儿（tūbǎogàir）	写、军、农
讠	言字旁儿（yánzìpángr）	认、该、语
卩	单耳旁儿（dān'ěrpángr） 单耳刀儿（dān'ěrdāor）	卫、却、印
阝	左耳刀儿（zuǒ'ěrdāor） 右耳刀儿（yòu'ěrdāor）	队、阳、院 那、都、邮
厶	私字儿（sīzìr）	么、云、去
廴	建之旁儿（jiànzhīpángr）	廷、建、诞
土	提土旁儿（títǔpángr）	场、地、坏
扌	提手旁儿（tíshǒupángr）	报、打、找

---

① Most of the character components in this book cannot make up characters on their own, nor are they easy to address or have the name accepted by all. Components that can make up Characters on their own or easy to address are not included in this book, for example, "山、马、女、日、月、鸟、虫、口", etc.

部 首 Radieals	名 称 Names	例 字 Examples
土	提土旁儿（títǔpángr）	场、地、坏
扌	提手旁儿（tíshǒupángr）	报、打、找
艹	草字头儿（cǎozìtóur） 草头儿（cǎotóur）	苹、葡、萄
廾	弄字底儿（nòngzìdǐr）	开、弄、弄
囗	国字框儿（guózìkuàngr）	国、因、困
业	尚字头儿（shàngzìtóur）	光、当、尚
彳	双人旁儿（shuāngrénpángr）	行、往、很
彡	三撇儿（sānpiěr）	须、影、参
犭	反犬旁儿（fǎnquǎnpángr）	狗、猪、猫
夂	折文儿（zhéwénr）	冬、处、各
饣	食字旁儿（shízìpángr）	饭、饱、饿
丬	将字旁儿（jiàngzìpángr）	将、状、妆
广	广字旁儿（guǎngzìpángr）	床、应、店
氵	三点水儿（sāndiǎnshuǐr）	波、法、海
忄	竖心旁儿（shùxīnpángr）	忙、快、怕
宀	宝盖儿（bǎogàir）	穴、字、宋
辶	走之儿（zǒuzhīr）	进、还、送
孑	子字旁儿（zǐzìpángr）	孔、孙、孩
纟	绞丝旁儿（jiǎosīpángr）	红、经、纸
王	王字旁儿（wángzìpángr） 斜玉旁儿（xiéyùpángr）	玩、环、球

部首 Radieals	名 称 Names	例 字 Examples
木	木字旁儿（mùzìpángr）	林、样、楼
牛	牛字旁儿（niúzìpángr）	牧、物、特
攵	反文旁儿（fǎnwénpángr）	改、教、数
爫	爪字头儿（zhǎozìtóur）	采、受、爱
火	火字旁儿（huǒzìpángr）	灯、炼、烧
灬	四点儿（sìdiǎnr）	点、然、照
礻	示字旁儿（shìzìpángr）	礼、视、祝
罒	四字头儿（sìzìtóur）	罚、罪、署
皿	皿字底儿（mǐnzìdǐr）	盆、盐、盘
钅	金字旁儿（jīnzìpángr）	钟、钱、锻
禾	禾木旁儿（hémùpángr）	利、秋、科
疒	病字旁儿（bìngzìpángr）	病、疼、痛
衤	衣字旁儿（yīzìpángr）	初、被、裤
覀	西字头儿（xīzìtóur）	要、票、粟
虍	虎字头儿（hǔzìtóur）	虎、彪、虢
竹	竹字头儿（zhúzìtóur）	第、等、答
丷	美字头儿（měizìtóur）	美、羞、善
羊	羊字旁儿（yángzìpángr）	差、着、羚
龹	卷字头儿（juànzìtóur）	卷、拳、眷
米	米字旁儿（mǐzìpángr）	粗、精、糕
足	足字旁儿（zúzìpángr）	跑、跳、路